Sticks and Bones

A PLAY IN TWO ACTS

by David Rabe

SAMUEL FRENCH

FOUNDED 1830

New York Hollywood London Toronto

SAMUELFRENCH.COM

Sticks and Bones

A PLAY IN TWO ACTS

by David Rabe

SAMUEL FRENCH

Also By David Rabe

THE BASIC TRAINING OF PAVLO HUMMEL

GOOSE AND TOM TOM

IN THE BOOM BOOM ROOM

THE ORPHAN

STREAMERS

Consult our *Basic Catalogue of Plays* for details.

New York Shakespeare Festival Public Theater presents:

Sticks and Bones by David Rabe

Produced by Joseph Papp, Directed by Jeff Bleckner, Setting by Santo Loquasto, Costumes by Theoni V. Aldredge, Lighting by Ian Calderon and Associate Producer Bernard Gersten

CAST

The Family:

OZZIE .... *Tom Aldredge*

HARRIET .... *Elizabeth Wilson*

DAVID .... *David Selby*

RICK .... *Cliff DeYoung*

THE SGT. MAJOR .... *Hector Elias*

THE PRIEST .... *Charles Siebert*

THE GIRL .... *Asa Gim*

TIME: Autumn, 1968

PLACE: The family home

CAST OF CHARACTERS

Ozzie

Harriet

Rick

David

Zung (The Girl)

Father Donald

The Sgt. Major

Sticks and Bones

ACT ONE

PLACE: *The family home.*

Darkness: Silence. Slides appear on either side of stage: black and white medium close-up of a young man, mood and clothing of the Nineteen Hundreds. He is lean, reasonably handsome, black hair parted in the center. Voices speak. They are slow and relaxed with an improvisational quality.

CHILD 1. Who's zat?

MALE ADULT. Grandpa Jacob's Father. (*Slide 2: Group photo, same era, eight or ten people, all ages.*)

CHILD 2. Look at 'em all!

CHILD 1. How come they're all so serious? (*Slide 3: Small boy, black hair, black knickers.*)

FEMALE ADULT. There's Grandpa Ozwald as a little boy.

CHILD 1. Grandpa? (*Slide 4: Different boy, same pose.*)

FEMALE ADULT. And that's his brother Thomas. He died real young.

MALE ADULT. Scarlet Fever. (*As there is a new slide: Young girl, 17 or 18.*) And that's his sister Christina.

FEMALE ADULT. No, that's Grandma.

MALE ADULT. No.

FEMALE ADULT. Sure. (*As there is a new slide:* OZZIE *and* HARRIET, *young, 1940s era.*) There's the two of them.

MALE ADULT. Mmmmm, you're right, because that's Grandpa. (*As there is a new slide, two young boys, 5 and 9 years old.*)

5

FEMALE ADULT. The taller one's David, right? (*New slide: Photo, close-up of* DAVID *from the last moment of the play, a stricken look.*)

CHILD 1. What's that one?

MALE ADULT. Somebody sick.

CHILD 1. Boy . . . ! (*New slide:* OZZIE, HARRIET *and* FATHER DONALD. FATHER DONALD, *wearing a Gym suit, his back to the camera, stands holding a basketball in one hand.* OZZIE *and* HARRIET *face him, one on either side.*)

CHILD 2. Oh, look at that one!

MALE ADULT. That's a funny one, isn't it.

FEMALE ADULT. That's one—I bet somebody took it— they didn't know it was going to be taken.

(*There is a bright flash and the stage is immediately illuminated. The set is an American home, very modern, a quality of brightness, green walls, green rug. There is naturalness, yet a sense of space and, oddly, a sense also that this room, these stairs belong in the gloss of an advertisement. Downstage, on wheels, a TV faces upstage, glowing, murmuring.* OZZIE, HARRIET, FATHER DONALD *are standing as they were in the slide last seen.*)

FATHER DONALD. A feel for it is the big thing. A feel for the ball. You know, I mean, bouncing it, dribbling it. You don't even look at it. (*PHONE RINGS.*)

OZZIE. I'll get it.

FATHER DONALD. You can do it, Harriet. Give it a try. (*Bouncing the ball to* HARRIET.)

OZZIE. —Hello?—

FATHER DONALD. (*As she catches it.*) —That a girl—

HARRIET. —Oh, Father,—

OZZIE. (*Hanging up.*) Nobody there.

FATHER DONALD. That's what I'm telling you. You gotta help kids. Keeps 'em outa trouble. We help Organized sports activities; it does 'em a world a good. You know that. And they need you.

OZZIE. Well, I was a decent basketball player—I could get

around, but my strong suit was track and field. I was quite a miler. Dash man. I told you, Father. (*TELEPHONE RINGS.*) I could throw the discus. (*As he runs for the phone.*)

FATHER DONALD. But this is basketball season. (*Moving for* HARRIET *and then the door as* OZZIE *goes to the phone, says "Hello", then listens intently.*) You listen to me, Harriet, you get husband of yours out there to help us. It'll do him good and he's the kind of man we need. Leaders. We need leaders.

HARRIET. Oh, Father Donald, bless me.

FATHER DONALD. Of course. (*He blesses her, holding the ball under his left arm.*) Bye, bye.

HARRIET. (*As* FATHER DONALD *goes.*) Goodbye, Father. (*And she turns to look for a moment at* OZZIE *on the phone.*) Why aren't you talking? (*Silence: she is looking at him.*) Ozzie, why aren't you talking?

OZZIE. (*Slowly lowering the phone.*) They're gone. They hung up.

HARRIET. You didn't say a word. You said nothing.

OZZIE. I said my name.

HARRIET. What did they want?

OZZIE. I said hello.

HARRIET. Were they selling something—is that what they wanted?

OZZIE. No, no.

HARRIET. Well . . . who was it?

OZZIE. What?

HARRIET. What are we talking about?

OZZIE. The Government. It was . . . you know. . . .

HARRIET. Ozzie! (*In fear.*) No!

OZZIE. (*Some weariness in him.*) No, he's all right, he's coming home!

HARRIET. Why didn't you let me speak? Who was it?

OZZIE. No, no.

HARRIET. It was David.

OZZIE. No, somebody else. Some clerk. I don't know who.

HARRIET. You're lying.

OZZIE. No. There was just all this static—it was hard

to hear. But he was coming home was part of it, and they had his records and papers but I couldn't talk to him directly even though he was right there, standing right there.

HARRIET. I don't understand.

OZZIE. That's what they said . . . and he was fine and everything. And he wanted them to say "Hello" for him. He'd lost some weight. He would be sent by truck. I could hear truck engines in the background—revving. They wanted to know my name. I told them.

HARRIET. No more?

OZZIE. They were very professional. Very brusque . . .

HARRIET. No more . . . at all . . . ?

(And the door opens and RICK comes in. He is young, 17; and the door slams. His hair is long and neat, sideburns. His clothing is elaborate, very very up to date. He carries a guitar on his shoulder.)

RICK. Hi, Mom, Hi, Dad.

HARRIET. Hi, Rick.

OZZIE. Hi, Rick.

HARRIET. Ohhh, Ricky, Ricky, your brother's on his way home. David's coming home!

OZZIE. We just got a call.

RICK. Ohhh, Boy!

HARRIET. Isn't that wonderful? Isn't it? Your father talked to him. Oh I bet you're starving, sit, sit.

OZZIE. I talked to *somebody*, Rick.

HARRIET. There's fudge and ice cream in the fridge, would you like that?

RICK. Oh, yeah, and could I have some soda? (*She is on her way to the kitchen, nodding.*) Wow; that sure is some news. I'm awful hungry.

OZZIE. Never had a doubt. A boy like that—if he leaves, he comes back.

RICK. How about me? What if I left? (*As he picks up a comic book.*)

OZZIE. Absolutely. Absolutely. (*Silence:* RICKY *reads the comic.*) I built jeeps . . . tanks, trucks.

RICK. What?

OZZIE. In the other war, I mean. Number Two. I worked on vehicles. Vehicles were needed and I worked to build them. Sometimes I put on wheels, tightened 'em up. I never . . . served . . . is what I mean. (*Slight pause.*) They got all those people—soldiers, Rick—you see what I mean? They get 'em across the ocean, they don't have any jeeps or tanks or trucks, what are they gonna do, stand around? Wait for a bus on the beachhead? Call a cab?

RICK. No public transportation in a war.

OZZIE. That's right, that's right. (*As* HARRIET *enters, carrying fudge and ice cream.*)

HARRIET. Oh, Ozzie, Ozzie, do you remember—I just remembered that time David locked himself in that old ice box. We didn't know where he was. We looked all over. We couldn't find him. And then there was this ice box in this clearing . . . out in the middle. I'll bet you don't even remember.

OZZIE. Of course I remember.

HARRIET. And he leaped to us. So frightened.

OZZIE. He couldn't even speak—he couldn't even speak—just these noises.

HARRIET. Or that time he fell from that tree.

OZZIE. My God, he was somethin'! If he wasn't fallin', he was gettin' hit.

HARRIET. And then there was that day we went out into the woods. It was just all wind and clouds. We sailed a kite!

OZZIE. I'd nearly forgotten . . . !

RICK. Where was I?

HARRIET. You were just a baby, Rick. We had a picnic.

RICK. I'm gonna get some more soda, okay? (HARRIET *touches him as he passes.*)

OZZIE. What a day that was. I felt great that day.

HARRIET. And then Hank came along. Hank Grenweller. He came from out of the woods calling that—

OZZIE. That's right.

HARRIET. He was happy.

OZZIE. We were all happy. And then we had that race. Wasn't that the day?

HARRIET. I don't remember.

OZZIE. Hank and me! Hank Grenweller. A foot race. And I beat him. I did it; got him.

HARRIET. Noooo.

OZZIE. It was only inches, but—

HARRIET. You know that's not true. If it was close— that race you ran—and it was— (*This is not loud: There is intimacy. They are near one another.*) I remember now—it was because he let it—no other reason. We were all having fun. He didn't want to make you feel badly.

RICK. (*Calling from the kitchen.*) You people want some fudge!

HARRIET. No Rick.

OZZIE. I don't know he didn't try. I don't know that. (*Staring at* HARRIET.)

HARRIET. I think I'll be going up to bed; take a little nap.

RICK. Sleepy, Mom?

HARRIET. A little. (*She is crossing toward* OZZIE.)

RICK. That's a good idea then.

HARRIET. Call me.

RICK. Okay.

HARRIET. Do you know, the day he left? It was a winter day. November, Ozzie. (*Moving toward the stairs.*)

OZZIE. I know.

HARRIET. I prayed; did you know that? Now he's home.

OZZIE. It was a winter day.

HARRIET. I know.

RICK. Night, Mom. (*He is toying with his guitar. She*

doesn't answer, disappears walking down the hall. He looks up, yells.) Night, Mom!

HARRIET. (*From off.*) Turn off the T.V. somebody.

(RICK *crosses to the T.V. He turns it off. He wheels it back under the stairs. OZZIE watches. Silence.*)

OZZIE. I knew she was praying. She moves her lips. (RICKY *does not look up. He begins, softly, to strum and tune the guitar.*) And something else—yes, sir, boy, oh, boy, I tell you, huh? What a day, huh? (*Slight pause.*) They got seventeen hundred million men they gotta deal with, how they gonna do that without any trucks and tanks and jeeps? But I'm some kinda jerk because I wasn't out there blastin' away, huh? I was useful. I put my time to use. I been in fights. Fat Kramer. How we used to fight. (RICKY *strums some notes on the guitar.* OZZIE *stares at him.*) How come I'm restless? I . . . seen him do some awful, awful things, ole Dave. He was a mean . . . foul-tempered little baby. I'm only glad I was *here* when they sent him off to do his killing. That's right. (*Silence.*) I feel like I swallowed ants, that's how restless I am. Outran a bowlin' ball one time. These guys bet me I couldn't do it and I did, beat it to the pins. Got a runnin' start, then the— (*A faint, strange rapping sound has stopped him, spun him around.*) Did you do that?

RICK. Somebody knockin'.

OZZIE. Knockin'?

RICK. The door, Dad.

OZZIE. Oh.

RICK. You want me to get it?

OZZIE. No, no. It's just so late. (*As he moves for the door.*)

RICK. That's all right.

OZZIE. Sure. (*Opening the door just a crack, as if to kind of stick his head around. But the door is thrust open and a man, Black or of Spanish descent enters dressed in the uniform of a SGT. MAJOR. He has many campaign ribbons. Perhaps he enters abruptly. Or perhaps more gradually, speaking at first off in the dark, his words slowly forcing* OZZIE *back and the door slowly open.*)

SGT. MAJOR. Excuse me. Listen to me. I'd like to speak to the father here. I'd like to know who . . . is the father? Could . . . you tell me the address?

OZZIE. May I ask who it is who's asking?

SGT. MAJOR. I am. I'm asking. What's the address of this house?

OZZIE. But I mean, who is it that wants to know?

SGT. MAJOR. We called; we spoke. Is this 717 Dunbar?

OZZIE. Yes.

SGT. MAJOR. What's wrong with you?

OZZIE. Don't you worry about me.

SGT. MAJOR. I have your son.

OZZIE. What?

SGT. MAJOR. Your son.

OZZIE. No.

SGT. MAJOR. But he is. I have papers, pictures, prints. I know your blood and his. This is the right address. Please. Excuse me. (*He pivots, reaches out into the dark.*) I am very busy. I have your father, David. (*Drawing* DAVID *in from the dark, a tall thin boy, blond and, in the shadows wearing sun-glasses and a uniform of dress greens. In his right hand is a long, white, red-tipped cane. He moves, probing the air, as the* SGT. MAJOR *moves him past* OZZIE *toward the couch where he will sit the boy down like a parcel.*)

OZZIE. Dave . . . ?

SGT. MAJOR. He's blind.

OZZIE. What?

SGT. MAJOR. Blind.

OZZIE. I don't . . . understand.

SGT. MAJOR. We're very sorry.

OZZIE. Ohhhhh. Yes. Ohhhh. (*Realizing.*) I see . . . sure. I mean, we didn't know. Nobody said it. I mean, sure, Dave, sure; it's all right—don't you worry. Rick's here too, Dave—Rick, your brother, tell him "Hello."

RICK. Hi, Dave.

DAVID. You said "Father." (*Worried.*)

OZZIE. Well . . . there's two of us, Dave; two.

DAVID. Sergeant, you said "home." I don't think so.

OZZIE. Dave, sure.

DAVID. It doesn't feel right.

OZZIE. But it is, Dave—me and Rick—Dad and Rick, Harriet! (*Calling up the stairs.*) Harriet!

DAVID. Let me touch their faces . . . I can't see. (*Rising, his fear increasing.*) Let me put my fingers on their faces.

OZZIE. (*Hurt, startled.*) What? Do what?

SGT. MAJOR. Will that be all right, if he does that?

OZZIE. Sure . . . Sure . . . Fine.

SGT. MAJOR. (*Helping DAVID to OZZIE.*) It will take him time.

OZZIE. That's normal and to be expected. I'm not surprised. Not at all. We figured on this. Sure, we did. Didn't we, Rick?

RICK. (*Occupied with his camera, an instamatic.*) I wanna take some pictures. How are you, Dave?

DAVID. What room is this?

OZZIE. Middle room, Dave. T.V. room. T.V.'s in—

HARRIET. David . . . ! Oh, David . . . ! (*She is on the stairs.*) David . . . (*And OZZIE hurries toward the stairs, leaving DAVID, looking up at her as she falters, stops, stares up and RICK moving near, snaps a picture of her.*)

OZZIE. Harriet . . . don't be upset . . . they say . . . Harriet, Harriet . . . he can't see . . . ! Harriet . . . they say—he—can't . . . see. That man.

HARRIET. (*As she is standing very still.*) Can't see? What do you mean?

SGT. MAJOR. He's blind.

HARRIET. No. Who says? No, no.

OZZIE. Look at him; he looks so old. But it's nothing, Harriet, I'm sure.

SGT. MAJOR. I hope you people understand.

OZZIE. It's probably just how he's tired from his long trip.

HARRIET. (*Moving toward him.*) Oh, you're home now, <u>David. You're home.</u>

SGT. MAJOR. (*With a large sheet of paper waving in his hands.*) Who's gonna sign this for me, Mister? It's a shipping receipt. I got to have somebody's signature to show you got him. I got to have somebody's name on the paper.

OZZIE. Let me. All right?

SGT. MAJOR. Just here and here, you see? Your name or mark three times.

(*As they move toward a table and away from* HARRIET *who is near* DAVID.)

OZZIE. Fine, listen, would you like some refreshments?

SGT. MAJOR. No.

OZZIE. I mean while I do this. Cake and coffee. Of course you do.

SGT. MAJOR. No.

OZZIE. Sure.

SGT. MAJOR. No. I haven't time. I've got to get going. I've got trucks out there backed up for blocks. Other boys. I got to get on to Chicago and some of them to Denver and Cleveland, Reno, New Orleans, Boston, Trenton, Watts, Atlanta. And when I get back they'll be layin' all over the grass; layin' there in pieces all over the grass, their backs been broken, their brains jellied, their insides turned into garbage. No-legged boys and one-legged boys. I'm due in Harlem; I got to get to the Bronx and Queens, Cincinnati, St. Louis, Reading. I don't have time for coffee. I got deliveries to make all across this country.

DAVID. Nooooooo . . . (*With* HARRIET, *his hands on her face, a kind of realization.*) Sergeant . . . nooo; there's something wrong; it all feels wrong. Where are you? Are you here? I don't know these people!

SGT. MAJOR. That's natural, Soldier; it's natural you feel that way.

DAVID. Nooooo.

HARRIET. (*He has risen; she is attempting to guide him back to a chair.*) David; just sit, be still.

DAVID. Don't you hear me?

OZZIE. Harriet, calm him.

DAVID. The air is wrong; the smells and sounds, the wind.

HARRIET. <u>David, please, please,</u> What is it? <u>Be still.</u> Please . . .

DAVID. GODDAMN YOU, SERGEANT, <u>I AM LONELY HERE</u>! I AM LONELY!

SGT. MAJOR. I got to go. (*And he pivots to leave.*)

DAVID. Sergeant! (*Following the sound of the* SGT. MAJOR'S *voice.*)

SGT. MAJOR. (*Whirling, bellowing.*) You shut up. You <u>piss-ass soldier</u>, you shut the fuck up!

OZZIE. (*Walking to the* SGT. MAJOR, *putting his hand on the man's shoulder.*) Listen, let me walk you to the door. All right? I'd like to take a look at that truck of yours. All right?

SGT. MAJOR. There's more than one.

OZZIE. Fine.

SGT. MAJOR. It's a convoy.

OZZIE. Good.

(*They exit, slamming the door, and* RICKY, *running close behind them, pops it open, leaps out. He calls from off.*)

RICK. Sure are lots a trucks, Mom!

HARRIET. Are there? (*As he re-enters.*)

RICK. Oh, yeah. Gonna rain some more too. (*And turning, he runs up the stairs.*) See you in the morning. 'Night, Dave.

HARRIET. It's so good to have you here again; so good to see you. <u>You look . . . just</u> (*As* OZZIE *has slipped*

back into the room behind her: he stands, looking.) . . .
fine. You look— (*And she senses his presence, turns, immediately, speaking.*) He bewilders you, doesn't he. (*And*
OZZIE, *jauntily, heads for the stairs.*) Where are you
going? (*And he stops; he doesn't know. And she is
happily sad now as she speaks, sad for poor* OZZIE *and*
DAVID, *they are so whimsical, so child-like.*) You thought
you knew what was right, all those years, teaching him
sports and fighting. Do you understand what I'm trying
to say? A mother knows *things* . . . a father cannot ever
know them. The measles, small pox, cuts and bruises.
Never have you come upon him in the night as he lay
awake and staring . . . praying.

OZZIE. I saw him put a knife through the skin of a cat.
I saw him cut the belly open.

DAVID. Noooo. . . .

HARRIET. (*Moving toward him in response.*) David,
David. . . .

DAVID. Ricky! (*There is a kind of accusation in this
as if he were saying* RICKY *did the killing of the cat. He
says it loudly and directly into her face.*)

HARRIET. He's gone to bed.

DAVID. I want to leave. (*There is furniture around
him; he is caged, he pokes with his cane.*)

HARRIET. What is it?

DAVID. Help me. (*He crashes.*)

OZZIE. Settle down! Relax.

DAVID. I want to leave! I want to leave! I want to
leave. I— (*And he smashes into the stairs, goes down,
flails, pounding his cane.*) want to leave.

OZZIE *and* HARRIET. Dave! David! Davey!

DAVID. . . . to leave! Please. (*He is on the floor,
breathing. Long, long silence in which they look at him
sadly until she announces the problem's solution.*)

HARRIET. Ozzie, get him some medicine. Get him some
Easy Sleep.

OZZIE. Good idea.

HARRIET. It's in the medicine cabinet; a little blue
bottle, little pink pills. (*And when* OZZIE *is gone up the*

stairs, there is quiet. She stands over him.) It'll give you the sleep you need, Dave; the sleep you remember. You're our child and you're home. Our good . . . beautiful boy. (*And the door to the outside bursts open. There is a small girl in the doorway, an* ASAIN GIRL. *She wears the Vietnamese Ao Dai, black slacks and white tunic slit up the sides. Slowly, she enters, carrying before her a small straw hat.* HARRIET *is looking at the open door.*) What an awful . . . wind. (*She shuts the door.*)

(*BLACKOUT. MUSIC. A match flickers as* HARRIET *lights a candle and in the night, the girl silently moves from before the door across the floor to the stairs where she sits as* HARRIET *moves toward the stairs.* OZZIE, *asleep sitting up in a chair, stirs.*)

HARRIET. Oh! I didn't mean to wake you. I lit a candle so I wouldn't wake you. (*He stares at her.*) I'm sorry.

OZZIE. I wasn't sleeping. (*As he turns on a flashlight.*)

HARRIET. I thought you were. (*Heading up the stairs.*)

OZZIE. Couldn't. Tried. Couldn't. Thinking. Thoughts running very fast. Trying to remember the night David . . . was made. Do you understand me? I don't know why. But the feeling was in me that I had to figure something out and if only I could remember that night, the mood . . . I would be able. You're shaking your head.

HARRIET. I don't understand.

OZZIE. No.

HARRIET. Good night. (*As* OZZIE, *with his flashlight goes out the front door. At* DAVID'S *door, she raps softly and then opens the door. To* DAVID, *lying unmoving on the bed, she says:*) I heard you call.

DAVID. What?

HARRIET. I heard you call.

DAVID. I didn't.

HARRIET. Would you like a glass of warm milk?

DAVID. I was sleeping.

HARRIET. (*After a slight pause.*) How about that milk? Would you like some milk?

DAVID. I didn't call. I was sleeping.

HARRIET. I'll bet you're glad you didn't bring her back. Their skins are yellow, aren't they?

DAVID. What?

HARRIET. You're troubled, warm milk would help. Do you pray at all anymore? If I were to pray now, would you pray with me?

DAVID. What . . . do you want?

HARRIET. They eat the flesh of dogs.

DAVID. I know. I've seen them.

HARRIET. Pray with me; pray.

DAVID. What do you want?

HARRIET. Just to talk, that's all. Just to know that you're home and safe again. Nothing else; only that we're all together, a family. You must be exhausted. Don't worry; sleep. (*She is backing into the hallway.*) Good night. (*A whisper; she blows out the candle and is gone moving up stairs that lead to additional second and third floor rooms. The girl enters, and* DAVID *sits up.*)

DAVID. Who's there? (*As she drifts by, he waves the cane at the air.*) Zung? (*He stands.*) Cho, Co Zung. (*He moves for the door which he opens and steps into the hall, leaving her behind him in the room.*) Zung. Cho, Co Zung. (*And he moves off up the hallway. She follows.*) Zung . . . ! (*BLACKOUT. MUSIC. LIGHTS UP: It is a bright afternoon, and* OZZIE *is under the stairs with a screwdriver in his hand as he pokes about at the T.V. set.*)

OZZIE. C'mon, c'mon. Ohhhh, c'mon, this one more game and ole State's Bowl bound. C'mon, what is it. Ohhh, hey . . . ohhhhh. . . .

HARRIET. (*As she enters, carrying a bowl.*) Ozzie, take this up to David, make him eat it.

OZZIE. Harriet, the T.V. is broke.

HARRIET. What?

OZZIE. There's a picture but no sound. I don't— (*Grabbing her by the arm, pulling her toward a place before the set.*)

HARRIET. Stoppit, you're spilling the soup. (*Pulling free.*)

OZZIE. It's Sunday. I want to watch it. I turned it on, picture came on just like normal. I got the volume up full blast. (*Having set the soup down, she now shoves the T.V. set deeper under the stairs, deeper into the place where it is kept when not in use.*) Hey! I want to watch it!

HARRIET. I want to talk about David.

OZZIE. David's all right. (*As he turns, crosses toward the phone; he picks up the phone book.*) I'm gonna call the repairman.

HARRIET. (*Following him. She will take the phone book from him.*) Ozzie, he won't eat. He just lays there. I offer him food, he won't eat it. No, no. The T.V. repairman won't help, you Silly. He doesn't matter. There's something wrong with David. He's been home days and days and still he speaks only when spoken to; there's no light in his eye, no smile, he's not happy to be here and not once has he touched me or held me nor has he even shaken your hand. (OZZIE *flops down in a chair.*)

OZZIE. Oh, I don't mind that. Why should I mind—

HARRIET. And now he's talking to himself! What about that? Do you mind that? He mutters in his sleep.

OZZIE. Ohhhhhh. (*Exasperated, denying her.*)

HARRIET. Yes. And it's not a regular kind of talking at all. It's very strange—very spooky.

OZZIE. Spooky?

HARRIET. That's right.

OZZIE. I never heard him.

HARRIET. You sleep too deeply. I took a candle and followed. I was in his room. He lay there, speaking.

OZZIE. Speaking what?

HARRIET. I don't know. I couldn't understand.

OZZIE. Was it words?

HARRIET. All kind of funny and fast.

OZZIE. Maybe prayer; praying.

HARRIET. No. No, it was secret. Oh, Ozzie, I know praying when I hear it and it wasn't praying he was doing. We meant our son to be so different—I don't understand—good and strong. And yet ·. . . perhaps he is. But there are moments when I see him . . . <u>hiding</u> . . . <u>in that bed behind those awful glasses</u> . . . and I see the <u>chalkiness</u> that's come into—

OZZIE. Those <u>glasses are simply to ease his discomfort.</u> (*Headed for the kitchen, looking for juice to drink.*)

HARRIET. I hate them.

OZZIE. They're tinted glass and plastic— Don't be so damn suspicious.

HARRIET. I'm not, I'm not. It's seeing I'm doing, not suspicion. Suspicion hasn't any reasons. It's you—now accusing me for no reason when I'm only worried.

OZZIE. Can I have some juice? (*Returning from the kitchen, angered.*)

HARRIET. I want to talk.

OZZIE. The hell with David for a minute—I want some juice.

HARRIET. Shut up. You're sefish. You're so selfish.

OZZIE. I'll walk over, I'll pour it on the floor. I'll break the glass. (*She turns to move to get the juice.*)

HARRIET. A few years ago you might have done that kind of thing.

OZZIE. I woke up this morning, I could see so clearly the lovely way you looked when you were young. Beside me this morning, you were having trouble breathing. You kept . . . trying . . . to breathe. (*As she is approaching him to hand him the juice.*) ·What do you give me when you give me this?

HARRIET. I always looked pretty much as I do now. I never looked so different at all.

DAVID. Good morning. (*Happy sounding, yet moving with urgency, he appears from off upstairs and decends toward them dressed in a red robe.*)

OZZIE. Oh, David, Ohhh, good morning. Hello. How

do you feel this fine bright morning; how do you feel?

DAVID. He was a big man, wasn't he?

OZZIE. What?

DAVID. Hank. You were talking about Hank Cren-weller. I thought you were.

OZZIE. Oh, yes. Hank. Very big. Big. A good fine friend, ole Hank.

DAVID. You felt when he was with you he filled the room.

OZZIE. It was the way he talked that did that. He boomed. His voice just boomed.

DAVID. He was here once and you wanted me to sit on his lap, isn't that right? It was after dinner. He was in a chair in the corner.

HARRIET. That's right.

DAVID. His hand was gone—the bone showed in the skin.

OZZIE. My God, what a memory—did you hear that, Harriet? You were only four or five. He'd just had this terrible awful auto accident. His hand was hurt, not gone.

DAVID. No. It was congenital.

OZZIE. What?

DAVID. That hand. The sickness in it.

OZZIE. Congenital?

DAVID. I'd like some coffee. (*He is seated now.*)

HARRIET. Of course. And what else with it?

DAVID. Nothing.

HARRIET. Oh, no, no, you've got to eat. To get back your strength. You must. Pancakes? How do pancakes sound? Or wheat cakes? Or there's eggs? And juice? Orange or prune: or waffles. I bet it's eggs you want. Over, David? Over easy? Scrambled?

DAVID. I'm only thirsty.

HARRIET. Well, all right then, coffee is what you'll have and I'll just put some eggs on the side; you used to love them so; remember? (*And picking up the tray, she is off toward the kitchen. Pause.*)

OZZIE. I mean, I hate to harp on a thing, but I just think you're way off base on Hank, Dave. I just think you're dead wrong.

DAVID. He told me.

OZZIE. Who?

DAVID. Hank.

OZZIE. You . . . talked to Hank?

DAVID. In California. The day before they shipped me overseas.

OZZIE. No, no. He went to Georgia when he left here. We have all his letters postmarked Georgia.

DAVID. It was California. I was in the barracks. The C.Q. came to tell me there was someone to see me. It was Hank asking did I remember him? He'd seen my name on a list and wondered if I was Ozzie's boy. He was dying, he said. The sickness was congenital. We had a long, long talk. (*There is great urgency in* DAVID.)

OZZIE. But his parents were good fine people, David.

DAVID. Don't you understand? We spoke.

OZZIE. Did he wanna know about me? Did he mention me?

DAVID. (*After thinking a moment.*) He asked . . . how you were.

OZZIE. Well, I'm fine. Sure. You told him. Fine. Fine.

HARRIET. (*Entering with a cup of coffee.*) It must be so wonderful for you to be home. It must just be so wonderful. A little strange, maybe . . . just a little, but time will take care of all that. It always does. You get sick and you don't know how you're going to get better and then you do. You just do. You must have terrible, awful ugly dreams, though. (*Slight pause.*)

OZZIE. She said you probably have terrible awful ugly dreams . . . though.

DAVID. What?

HARRIET. Don't you remember when we spoke last night?

DAVID. Who?

HARRIET. You called to me and then you claimed you hadn't.

DAVID. I didn't.

HARRIET. Ohhh, we had a lovely conversation, David. Of course you called. You called, we talked. We talked and laughed and it was very pleasant. Could I see behind your glasses?

DAVID. What? Do . . . what? (*Moving away, crossing in flight from them.*)

HARRIET. See behind your glasses; see your eyes.

OZZIE. Me too, Dave; could we?

DAVID. My eyes . . . are ugly.

OZZIE. We don't mind.

HARRIET. We're your parents, David.

DAVID. I think it better if you don't.

OZZIE. And something else I've been meaning to ask you—why did you cry out against us that first night—to that stranger, I mean, that Sergeant?

HARRIET. And you do dream. You do.

OZZIE. Sure. You needn't be ashamed.

HARRIET. We all do it. All of us.

OZZIE. We have things that haunt us.

HARRIET. And it would mean nothing at all—it would be of no consequence at all—if only you didn't speak.

DAVID. I don't understand.

OZZIE. She says she heard you, Dave.

HARRIET. I stood outside your door.

DAVID. No.

OZZIE. A terrible experience for her, Dave; you can see that.

HARRIET. Whatever it is, David, tell us.

OZZIE. What's wrong?

DAVID. No.

HARRIET. We'll work it out.

OZZIE. You can't know how you hurt us.

DAVID. I wasn't asleep.

OZZIE. Not until you have children of your own.

HARRIET. What? (*Silence.*) Not . . . asleep . . . ?

DAVID. I was awake; lying awake and speaking.

OZZIE. Now wait a minute.

DAVID. Someone was with me—there in the dark—I don't know what's wrong with me?

HARRIET. It was me. I was with you. There's nothing wrong with you.

DAVID. No. In my room. I could feel it.

HARRIET. I was there. (*And they have him cornered in another chair.*)

DAVID. No.

OZZIE. Harriet, wait!

HARRIET. What are you saying, "Wait"? I was there.

OZZIE. Oh, my God. Oh, Christ, of course. Oh, Dave, forgive us.

HARRIET. What?

OZZIE. Dave, I understand. It's buddies left behind.

DAVID. No!

OZZIE. But I do. Maybe your mother can't but I can. Men serving together in war, it's a powerful thing—and I don't mean to sound like I think I know it—all of it, I mean—I don't, I couldn't—but I respect you having had it—I almost envy you having had it, Dave. I mean . . . true comradeship.

DAVID. Dad . . .

OZZIE. I had just a taste—not that those trucks and factory were any battlefield, but there was a taste of it there—in the jokes we told and the way we saw each other first in the morning. We told dirty filthy jokes, Dave, we shot pool, played cards, drank beer late every night, singing all these crazy songs.

DAVID. That's not right, Dad.

OZZIE. But all that's nothing, I'm sure, to what it must be in war. The things you must touch and see. Honor. You must touch honor. And then one of you is hurt, wounded . . . made blind . . .

DAVID. No. I had fear of all the kinds of dying that there are when I went from here. And then there was this girl with hands and hair like wings. There were candles above the net of gauze under which we lay. Lizards. Cannon could be heard. A girl to weigh no more than dust.

HARRIET. A nurse, right . . . David?

OZZIE. No, no, one of them foreign correspondents, English maybe or French. (*Silence.*)

HARRIET. Oh, how lovely! A WAC or Red Cross girl . . . ?

DAVID. No.

OZZIE. Red head or blonde, Dave?

DAVID. No.

(HARRIET *is shaken.*)

OZZIE. I mean, what you mean is you whored around a lot. Sure. ~~You whored around.~~ That's what you're saying. You banged some whores . . . Had some intercourse. Sure, I mean, that's my point. (DAVID, *turning away, seems about to rise.*) Now Dave, take is easy. What I mean is, okay, sure, you shacked up with. I mean, hit on. Hit on, Dave. Dicked. Look at me. I mean, you pronged it, right? Right? Sure, attaboy. (*Patting* DAVID *on the shoulder.*) Look, Dave, what are you doing? (*A rage is building in* DAVID, *tension forcing him to stand, his cane pressing the floor.*) We can talk this over. We can talk this over. (*Heading for the stairs,* DAVID *crashes into* OZZIE.) Don't—goddamnit, don't walk away from me. (*He pushes* DAVID *backward.*) What the hell do you think you're doing? It's what you did. Who the hell you think you are? You screwed it. A yellow whore. Some yellow ass. You put in your prick and humped your ass. You screwed some yellow fucking whore! (*He has chased* DAVID *backward,* HARRIET *joining in with him.*)

HARRIET. That's right, that's right. You were lonely and young and away from home for the very first time in your life, no white girls around—

DAVID. They are the color of the earth! What is white but winter and the earth under it like a suicide? (HARRIET'S *voice is a high humming in her throat.*) Why didn't you tell me what I was? (*And she vomits, her hands at her mouth, her back turning. There is a silence. They stand.* OZZIE *starts toward her, falters, starts, reaches, stops.*)

OZZIE. Why . . . don't . . . you ask her to cook something for you, David, will you? Make her feel better . . . okay.

DAVID. I think . . . some eggs might be good, Mom.

OZZIE. (*Wanting to help her.*) Hear that, Harriet? David wants some eggs.

HARRIET. I'm *all right.*

OZZIE. Of course you are. (*Patting her tenderly, he offers his clean white handkerchief.*) Here, here: wipe your mouth; you've got a little something—on the corner; left side. That's it. Whattayou say, David?

HARRIET. What's your pleasure, David?

DAVID. Scrambled.

OZZIE. There you go. Your specialty, his pleasure. (OZZIE, *between them, claps his hands; off she goes for the kitchen, and* OZZIE, *looking about the room like a man in deep water looking for something to keep him afloat, sees a pack of cigarettes.*) How about a cigarette? Filter, see, I switched. (*Running to grab them, show them.*) Just a little after you left, and I just find them a lot smoother, actually; I wondered if you'd notice. (*And speaking now, his voice and manner take on a confidence; he demonstrates; he is self-assured.*) The filter's granulated. It's an off-product of corn husks. I light up— I feel like I'm on a ship at sea. Isn't that one hell of a good tasting cigarette? Isn't that one beautiful Goddamn cigarette? (HARRIET *enters with two bowls. One has a grapefruit cut in half; the second has eggs and a spoon sticking out.*

HARRIET. Here's a little grapefruit to tide you over till I get the eggs. (*And now she stirs the eggs in preparation of scrambling them.*) Won't be long, I promise—but I was just wondering wouldn't it be nice if we could all go to church tonight. All together and we could make a little visit in thanksgiving of your coming home. (*He is putting his cigarette out in his grapefruit. They see.*) I wouldn't ask that it be long—just— (*He is rising now, dropping the grapefruit on the chair.*) I mean, we could go to whatever saint you wanted, it wouldn't . . . matter . . . (*He has turned his back, is walking toward the stairs.*) Just in . . . just out . . . (*He is climbing the stairs.*) David.

OZZIE. Tired . . . Dave? (*They watch him plodding unfalteringly for his door.*) Where are you going . . . bathroom? (*And* DAVID *enters his room, shutting the door.* HARRIET *whirls and heads for the phone,* OZZIE *turns to watch her, startled.*) Harriet, what's up?

HARRIET. I'm calling Father Donald.

OZZIE. Father Donald?

HARRIET. We need help, I'm calling for help.

OZZIE. Now wait a minute. No; oh, no, we—

HARRIET. Do you still refuse to see it: He was involved with one of them. You know what the Bible says about these people. You heard him.

OZZIE. Just not Father Donald; please, please. That's all I ask—just— (*She is obstinate, he sees; she turns her back, waiting for someone to answer.*) Why must everything be personal vengeance? (*And the door pops open and in comes bounding* RICK, *guitar upon his back.*)

RICK. Hi, Mom; Hi, Dad. (*Happy.*)

HARRIET. (*Waiting, telephone in hand.*) Hi, Rick! (*Over-joyed.*)

RICK. Hi, Mom. (*Happy.*)

OZZIE. Hi, Rick. (*Feeling fine.*)

RICK. Hi, Dad.

OZZIE. How you doin', Rick? (*He is happy to see good ole regular* RICK.)

RICK. Fine, Dad. You?

OZZIE. Fine.

RICK. Good.

HARRIET. I'll get you some fudge in just a minute, Rick!

RICK. Okay. How's Dave doin', Dad? (*He is fiddling with his camera.*)

OZZIE. Dave's doin' fine, Rick.

RICK. Boy, I'm glad to hear that. I'm really glad to hear that, because, boy, I'll sure be glad when everything's back to the regular way. Dave's too serious, Dad; don't you think so? That's what I think. Whattayou think, Dad? (*He snaps a picture of* OZZIE *who is posing, smiling while* HARRIET *waves angrily at them.*)

HARRIET. SHHHHHHH! EVERYBODY! (*And then, more pleasantly she returns to the phone.*) Yes, yes. Oh, Father, I didn't recognize your voice. No, I don't know who. Well, yes, it's about my son, Father, David. Yes. Well, I don't know if you know it or not, but he just got back from the war and he's troubled. Deeply. Yes. (*As she listens silently for a moment* RICK, *crouching, snaps a picture of her. She tries to wave him away.*) Deeply. (*He moves to another position, another angle, and snaps another picture.*) Deeply, yes. Oh. So do you think you might be able to stop over some time soon to talk to him or not? Father, any time that would be convenient for you. Yes. Oh, that would be wonderful. Yes. Oh, thank you. And may God reward *you*, Father. (*Hanging up the phone, she stands a moment, dreaming as* OZZIE *is pacing, talking to her.*)

OZZIE. I say to myself, what does it mean that he is my son? How the hell is it that . . . he . . . is my son? I mean, they say something of you joined to something of me and became . . . him . . . but what kinda goddamn thing is that? One **mystery** replacing another? Mystery doesn't explain mystery!

RICK. Mom, hey, c'mon, how about that fudge? (*Scarcely having looked up from his comic.*)

HARRIET. Ricky, oh, I'm sorry. I forgot.

OZZIE. They've got . . . diseases . . . !

HARRIET. What . . . ? (*Having been stopped by his voice.*)

OZZIE. Dirty, filthy deseases. They got 'em. Those girls. Infection. From the blood of their parents into the very fluids of their bodies. Malaria, T.B. An actual rot alive in them . . . gonorrhea, syphilis. There are some who have the plague. He touched them. It's disgusting.

RICK. Mom, I'm starving, honest to God; and I'm thirsty too.

HARRIET. (*As she scurries off, clapping, for the kitchen.*) Yes, of course. Oh, oh.

RICK. And bring a piece for Dad, too; Dad looks hungry.

OZZIE. No.

RICK. Sure, a big sweet chocolate piece a fudge.

OZZIE. No. Please. I don't feel well.

RICK. It'll do you good.

HARRIET. (*Entering with fudge and milk in each hand.*) Ricky, here, come here.

RICK. (*Hurrying toward her.*) What?

HARRIET. (*As she hands him fudge and milk.*) Look good? (*And moves toward* OZZIE.)

OZZIE. And something else—maybe it could just be that he's growing away from us, like we did ourselves from our own parents, only we thought it would happen in some other way, some—

HARRIET. (*Putting the fudge and milk into* OZZIE'S *hands.*) What are you talking about, 'going away'—he's right upstairs.

OZZIE. I don't want that.

HARRIET. You said you did.

OZZIE. He said I did.

RICK. (*Having gobbled the fudge and milk.*) You want me to drive you, Mom?

HARRIET. Would you, Ricky, please?

RICK. (*Running.*) I'll go around and get the car.

HARRIET. (*Scolding, as* OZZIE *has put the fudge and milk down on a coffee table.*) It's all cut and poured. Ozzie; it'll just be a waste.

OZZIE. I don't care.

HARRIET. You're so childish. (*As she marches off toward the door where she takes a light jacket from a hook, starts to slip it on.*)

OZZIE. Don't you know I could throw you down onto

this floor and make another child live inside you . . .
now . . . !

HARRIET. I . . . doubt that . . . Ozzie.

OZZIE. You want me to do it?

HARRIET. (*Going out the door.*) Ohhh, Ozzie, Ozzie. (*The door slams shut.*)

OZZIE. They think they know me and they know nothing.
They don't know how I feel . . . How I'd like to beat Ricky
with my fists till his face is ugly! How I'd like to banish David
to the streets . . . How I'd like to cut her tongue from her
mouth . . . ! (DAVID *moves upstairs.*) They know nothing . . . ! I was myself. (*And now it is clear he is talking to the audience, making them see his value. They are his friends, his buddies.*) I lived in a time beyond anything they can
ever know—a time beyond and separate and I was nobody's Goddamn father and nobody's Goddamn husband!
I was myself! And I could run. I got a scrapbook of victories; a bag of medals and ribbons. Nobody was faster.
In the town in which I lived my name was spoken in the
factories and in the fields all around because I was the
best there was. I'd beaten the finest anybody had to offer.
Summer . . . I would sit out on this old wood porch on
the front of our house and my strength was in me, quiet
and mine. Around the corner would come some old Model
T Ford and scampering up the walk this ancient bone-
stiff buck-toothed farmer raw as winter and cawing at me
like a crow: they had one for me. Out at the edge of town.
A runner from another county. My shoes are in a brown
paper bag at my feet and I snatch it up and set out into
the dusk, easy as breathing. There's an old white fence
and we run for the sun . . . For a hundred yards or a
thousand yards or a thousand thousand. It doesn't matter.
Whatever they want. We run the race they think their
specialty and I beat them. They sweat and struggle, I
simply glide on one step beyond . . . no matter what
their effort and the sun bleeds before me . . . We cross
rivers and deserts: we clamber over mountains. I run the

races the farmers arrange and win the bets they make; and then a few days after the race money comes to me anonymously in the mail; but it's not for the money that I run. In the fields and factories, they speak my name when they sit down to their lunches. If there's a (*As* DAVID, *entering from his room has listened to the latter part of this.*) prize to be run for, it's me they send for. It's to be the-one-sent-for that I run.

DAVID. (*Now at the top of the stairs.*) And . . . then . . . you left.

OZZIE. What? (*Whirling back.*)

DAVID. I said . . . "And . . . then you left." That town.

OZZIE. Left?

DAVID. Yes. Went away; traveled.

OZZIE. No. What do you mean?

DAVID. I mean, you're no longer there; you're here . . . now.

OZZIE. But I didn't really *leave* it. I mean, not *leave*. Not really.

DAVID. Of course you did. Where are you?

OZZIE. That's not the point, Dave. Where I am isn't the point at all.

DAVID. But it is. It's everything; all that other is gone. Where are you going?

OZZIE. Groceries. Gotta go get groceries. You want anything at the grocery store? (*He looks at his watch.*) It's late. I gotta get busy.

DAVID. (*As* OZZIE *exits.*) That's all right, Dad. That's fine.

BLACKOUT

(*Now the lights are rising to a brightness and* RICKY *enters, carrying his guitar, plinking a note or two as* HARRIET *emerges from the kitchen, carrying a bowl of chips as* OZZIE *appears upstairs, coming down the hall, carrying an 8mm movie projector already loaded with film.*)

HARRIET. Tune her up now, Rick.

OZZIE. What's the movie about, anyway?

HARRIET. It's probably scenery, don't you think?—trees and fields and those little ponds. Everything over there's so green and lovely. Enough chips, Ricky. (*All during this, they scurry about with their many preparations.*)

RICK. We're gonna have pretzels too. 'Cause if there's both pretzels and chips then there's enough chips.

OZZIE. David shoot it or somebody else . . . ? Anybody know? I tried to peek—put a couple feet up to the light . . . (*He is at the projector.*)

HARRIET. What did you see?

OZZIE. Nothing. Couldn't.

HARRIET. Well, I'll just bet there's one of those lovely little ponds in it somewhere.

OZZIE. Harriet . . . you know when David was talking about that trouble in Hank's hand being congenital, what did you think? You think it's possible? I don't myself. I mean, we knew Hank well. I think it's just something David got mixed up about and nobody corrected him. What do you think? Is that what you think? Whatsamatter? Oh. (*Stopping, startled as he sees she is waving at him. Looking up the stairs which are behind him, he sees* DAVID *is there, preparing to descend.* DAVID *wears his robe and a bright colored tie.*)

HARRIET. Hello!

OZZIE. Oh. Hey, oh, let me give you a hand. Yes. Yes. You look good. Good to see you. (*And he is on the move to* DAVID *to help him down the stairs.*) Yes, sir. I think, all things considered, I think we can figure we're over the hump now and it's all down hill and good from here on in. I mean, we've talked things over, Dave, what do you say?—The air's been cleared, that's what I mean—the wounds acknowledged, the healing begun. It's the ones that aren't acknowledged—the ones that aren't talked over—they're the ones that do the deep damage. That's always what happens.

HARRIET. (*Moving to* DAVID.) I've baked a cake, David. Happy, happy being home. (DAVID, *on his own, finds his way to a chair and sits.*)

OZZIE. And we've got pop and ice and chips and Rick is going to sing some songs.

HARRIET. Maybe we can all sing along if we want.

RICK. Anything special you'd like to hear, Dave?

OZZIE. You just sing what you know, Rick; sing what you care for and you'll do it best. (*As he and* HARRIET *settle down upon the couch to listen, all smiles.*)

RICK. How about "Baby, When I Find You"?

HARRIET. Ohhh, that's such a good one.

RICK. Dave, you just listen to me go! I'm gonna build! (*And there is an excited lead into the song.*) I'm gonna build, build, build. (*And he sings.*)

> Baby, when I find you,
> never, gonna stand behind you,
> gonna, gonna lead you
> softly at the start,
> gently by the heart,
> Sweet . . . Love . . . !
>
> Slipping softly to the sea
> you and me both mine
> wondrous as a green
> growing forest vine . . .
>
> Baby, when I find you,
> never, gonna stand behind you,
> gonna, gonna lead you
> softly at the start,
> gently by the heart,
> Sweet . . . Love . . . !
> Baby, when I find you.

OZZIE. (*As both he and* HARRIET *clap and laugh.*) Ohhh, great, Rick, great, you burn me up with envy, honest to God.

HARRIET. It was just so wonderful. Oh, thank you so much.

RICK. I just love to do it so much, you know?

OZZIE. Has he got something goin' for him, Dave? Huh? Hey! You don't even have a drink. Take this one; take mine! (*Now they hurry back and forth from* DAVID *to the table.*)

HARRIET. And here's some cake.

OZZIE. How 'bout some pretzels, Dave?

RICK. Tell me what you'd like to hear.

DAVID. I'd like to sing. (*This stops them. They stare at* DAVID *for a beat of silence.*)

RICK. What?

OZZIE. What's that?

DAVID. I have something I'd like to sing.

RICK. Dave, you don't sing.

DAVID. (*Reaching at the air.*) I'd like to use the guitar, if I could.

HARRIET. What are you saying?

OZZIE. C'mon, you couldn't carry a tune in a bucket and you know it. Rick's the singer, Rick and your mom. (*Not really listening, thinking that his father has gotten everything back to normal,* RICK *strums and strums the guitar, drifting nearer to* DAVID.) C'mon, let's go, that all we're gonna hear.

DAVID. You're so selfish, Rick; your hair is black; it glistens. You smile. You sing. People think you are the songs you sing. They never see you. Give me the guitar. (*And he clamps his hand closed on the guitar, stopping the music.*)

RICK. Mom, what's wrong with Dave?

DAVID. Give me.

RICK. Listen, you eat your cake and drink your drink and if you still wanna, I'll let you. (DAVID *stands, straining to the take the guitar.*)

DAVID. Now!

HARRIET. Ozzie, make David behave.

OZZIE. Don't you play too roughly. . . .

DAVID. Ricky . . . !

RICK. I don't think he's playing, Dad.

(*As* DAVID, *following* RICK, *bumps into a chair.*)

OZZIE. You watch out what you're doing . . . (DAVID *drops his glass on the floor, grabs the guitar.*)

RICK. You got cake all over your fingers, you'll get it all sticky, the strings all sticky— (*Struggling desperately to keep his guitar.*) Just tell me what you want to hear, I'll do it for you!

HARRIET. What is it? What's wrong?

DAVID. GIVE ME! (*As there is great anger in him.*) GIVE ME!

OZZIE. David . . . !

(*And* DAVID *wrenches the guitar from* RICKY's *hands, sends* RICKY *sprawling and loops the strap of the guitar over his shoulder, smiling, smiling.*)

HARRIET. Ohhhh, no, no, you're ruining everything. What's wrong with you?

OZZIE. I thought we were gonna have a nice party—

DAVID. I'm singing! We are!

OZZIE. No, no, I mean a *nice* party—one where everybody's happy!

DAVID. I'm happy. I'm singing. Don't you see them? Don't you see them?

OZZIE. Pardon, Dave?

HARRIET. What . . . are you saying?

DAVID. (*Changing, turning.*) I have home movies. I thought you . . . knew.

HARRIET. Well . . . we . . . do.

OZZIE. Movies?

DAVID. Yes, I took them.

RICK. I thought you wanted to sing.

OZZIE. I mean, they're what's planned, Dave. That's what's up. The projector's all wound and ready. I don't know what you had to get so angry for.

HARRIET. Somebody set up the screen.

OZZIE. Sure, sure. No need for all that yelling.

DAVID. I'll narrate.

OZZIE. Fine, sure. What's it about, anyway?

HARRIET. Are you in it?

OZZIE. Ricky, plug it in. C'mon, c'mon.

DAVID. It's a kind of story.

RICK. What about my guitar?

DAVID. No.

OZZIE. We oughta have some popcorn, though.

HARRIET. Oh, yes, what a dumb movie house, no popcorn, huh, Rick!

(RICK *switches off the lights.*)

OZZIE. Let her rip, Dave. (DAVE *turns on the projector;* OZZIE *is hurrying back to a seat.*) Ready when you are, C.B.

HARRIET. SHHHHHHH!

OZZIE. Let her rip, C.B. I want a new contract, C.B.

(*He is a little child playing: the projector has been running for a moment. [*NOTE: *in proscenium, let it seem the film is projected on the fourth wall. In three-quarter or round, a screen may be necessary, but nothing must show upon it but a flickering of green. If possible in procenium, the screen should be used.*)

HARRIET. Ohhh, what's the matter? It didn't come out, there's nothing there.

DAVID. Of course there is.

HARRIET. Noooo . . . It's all funny.

DAVID. Look.

OZZIE. It's underexposed, Dave.

DAVID. No. Look. (*Moving nearer.*)

HARRIET. What?

DAVID. They hang in the trees. They hang by their wrists half-severed by the wire.

OZZIE. Pardon me, Dave?

HARRIET. I'm going to put on the lights.

DAVID. NOOOOOO! LOOK! (*He uses his cane to point to the flickering screen with great specificity as if the events are there.*) They hang in the greenish haze afflicted by insects; a woman and a man, middle aged, they do not shout or cry. He is too small. Look: he seems all bone, shame in his eyes; his wife even here come with him, skinny also as a broom and her hair is straight and black, hanging to mask her eyes. (*As ZUNG drifts into the room.*)

OZZIE. I don't know what you're doing, David; there's nothing—

DAVID. LOOK! (*And he points.*) They are all bone and pain, uncontoured and ugly but for the peculiar melon-swelling in her middle which is her pregnancy—which they do not see— Look! These soldiers who have found her, as they do not see that she is not dead but only dying until saliva and blood bubble at her lips. Look . . . Yet . . . she dies. Though a doctor is called in to remove the bullet shot baby she would have preferred . . . to keep since she was dying and it was dead. (*And ZUNG silently, drifting, picks up a soda and drinks watching the movie.*) In fact, as it turned out they would have all been better off left to hang as they had been strung on the wire – he with the back of his head blown off and she (the rifle jammed exactly and deeply up into her) with a bullet fired directly into the child living there. For they ended each buried in a separate place; the husband by chance alone was returned to their village while the wife was dumped into an alien nearby plot of dirt, while the child, too small a piece of meat, was burned. (*He strums the guitar*) He into fire as the shattered legs and arms cut off of men are burned. There's an oven. It is no ceremony. It is the disposal of garbage . . . ! (HARRIET *gets to her feet, marches to the projector, pulls the plug, begins her little lecture.*)

HARRIET. It's so awful the things those yellow people do to one another. Yellow people hanging yellow people. Isn't that right? Ozzie, I told you—animals—Christ, burn them. David, don't let it hurt you. All the things you saw. People aren't themselves in war. I mean like that sticking that gun into that poor woman and then shooting that poor little baby, that's not human. That's inhuman. It's inhuman, barbaric and uncivilized and inhuman.

DAVID. I'm thirsty.

HARRIET. For what? Tell me. Water? Or would you like some milk? How about some milk? (*As he is shaking his head.*)

DAVID. No.

HARRIET. Or would you like some orange juice. All golden and little bits of ice.

OZZIE. Just all those words and that film with no picture and these poor people hanging somewhere—so you can bring them home like this house is a meat house—

HARRIET. Oh, Ozzie, no, it's not that—no—he's just young, a young boy . . . and he's been through terrible terrible things and now he's home, with his family he loves, just trying to speak to those he loves—just—

DAVID. Yes! That's right; yes. What I mean is, yes, of course, that's what I am—a young . . . blind man in a room . . . in a house in the dark, raising nothing in a gesture of no meaning toward two voices who are not speaking . . . of a certain . . . incredible . . . *connection!*

RICK. (*All stare; and* RICK *leaps up, running for the stairs.*) Listen, everybody, I hate to rush off like this, but I gotta. Night.

OZZIE and HARRIET. Goodnight, Rick. Goodnight.

(*As* DAVID *has been moving toward the stairs, looking upward.*)

DAVID. Because I talk of certain things . . . , don't think I did them. Murderers don't even know that murder happens.

HARRIET. What are you saying? No, no. We're a family, that's all—we've had a little trouble—David, you've got to stop – please – no more yelling. Just be happy and home like all the others – why can't you?

DAVID. (*Strumming the guitar he sings.*) You mean take some old man to a ditch of water, shove his head under, and talk of cars and money till his feeble pawing stops and then head on home to go in and out of doors and drive cars and sing sometimes. (*He stops singing.*) I left her like you wanted . . . where people are thin and small all their lives. (*The beginning of realization.*) Or did . . . you . . . think it was a . . . place . . . like this? Sinks and kitchens all the world over? Is that what you believe? Water from faucets, light from wires? Trucks, telephones, T.V. Ricky sings and sings, but if I were to cut his throat, he would no longer and you would miss him—you would miss his singing. We are hoboes! (*And it is the first time in his life he has ever thought these things.*) We make . . . signs . . . in the dark. You know yours. I understand my own. We share . . . coffee! (*There is nearly joy in this discovery: a hint of new freedom that might be liberation. And somewhere in the thrill of it, he was whirled, his cane has come near to* OZZIE, *frightening him, though* HARRIET *does not notice. Now* DAVID *turns, moving for the stairs, thinking.*) I'm going up to bed . . . now. . . . I'm very . . . tired.

OZZIE. Well . . . , you have a good sleep, son. . . .

DAVID. Yes, I think I'll sleep in. (*The girl following him up the stairs into his room.*)

OZZIE. You do as you please. . . .

DAVID. Goodnight.

HARRIET. Goodnight.

OZZIE. Goodnight.

HARRIET. Goodnight. (*Slight pause.*) You get a good rest. (*Silence.*) Try . . . (*Silence; they stand.*) I'm . . . hungry . . . Ozzie. . . . Are you hungry?

OZZIE. Hungry . . . ?

HARRIET. Yes.

OZZIE. No. Oh, no.

HARRIET. How do you feel? You look a little peaked. Do you feel all right?

OZZIE. I'm fine; I'm fine.

HARRIET. You look funny.

OZZIE. Really. No. How about yourself?

HARRIET. I'm never sick; you know that. Just a little sleepy.

OZZIE. Well, that's no wonder. It's been a long day.

HARRIET. Yes, it has.

OZZIE. No wonder.

HARRIET. Goodnight. (*She is climbing the stairs toward bed.*)

OZZIE. Goodnight.

HARRIET. Don't stay up too late now.

OZZIE. Do you know when he pointed that cane at me. I couldn't breathe. I felt for an instant I might never breathe. . . .

HARRIET. Ohhh, I'm so sleepy. So, sooooo sleepy. Aren't you sleepy?

OZZIE. (*To make her answer.*) Harriet! I couldn't breathe.

HARRIET. WHAT DO YOU WANT? TEACHING HIM SPORTS AND FIGHTING. (*In the whole of the First Act, this moment—it is almost a primal rage—should be the first shattering of her motherly, self-sacrificing image.*) WHAT . . . OZZIE . . . Do YOU WANT?

OZZIE. Well . . . I was wondering . . . do we have any aspirin down here . . . or are they all upstairs?

HARRIET. I thought you said you felt well.

OZZIE. Well, I do. It's just a tiny headache. Hardly worth mentioning.

HARRIET. There's aspirin in the desk.

OZZIE. (*Crossing.*) Big drawer?

HARRIET. Second drawer, right hand side.

OZZIE. Get me a glass of water, would you, please?

HARRIET. Of course. (*Getting a nearby glass left over from the party.*)

OZZIE. Thank you. It's not much of a headache, actually. Actually, it's just a tiny headache. (*He pops the pills into his mouth and drinks to wash them down.*)

HARRIET. Aspirin makes your stomach bleed. (*He tries but cannot stop.*) Did you know that? Nobody knows why. It's part of how it works. It just does it; makes you bleed. This extremely tiny series of hemorrhages in those delicate inner tissues. (*He is staring at her: there is vengeance in what she is doing.*) It's like those thin membranes begin, in a very minor way to sweat blood and you bleed; inside yourself you bleed. (*She crosses away.*)

OZZIE. That's not true. None of that. You made all that up . . . Where are you going? (*With a raincoat on, she is moving out the door.*) I mean . . . are you going out? Where . . . are you off to? (*She is gone.*) Goddamnit, there's something going on around here, don't you want to know what it is? (*Yelling at the shut door.*) I want to know what it is. (*Turning, marching to the phone, dialing.*) I want to know what's going on around here. I do. Want to—got to. Police. That's right, goddamnit— I want one of you people to get on out to 717 Dunbar and do some checking, some checking at 717— What? Ohhh— (*Hissing.*) Christ . . . ! (*And he is pulling a handkerchief from his pocket, he is covering the mouthpiece.*) I mean, they got a kid living there who just got back for the war and something's going on and I want to know what it— No, I don't wanna give my name— it's them, not me— Hey! Hey!

RICK. (*Popping in at the top of the hallway.*) Hey, Dad! How you doin'?

OZZIE. Oh, Rick! Hi!

RICK. Hi! How you doin'? (*He is heading down the stairs and toward the door.*)

OZZIE. Fine. Juse fine.

RICK. Good.

OZZIE. How you doin', Rick?

RICK. Well, I'll see you later.

OZZIE. (*Running with the guitar* DAVID *left.*) I WANT YOU TO TEACH ME GUITAR!

RICK. What? (*Faltering.*)

OZZIE. I want you to teach me . . . guitar . . . ! To play it.

RICK. Sure. Okay.

OZZIE. I want to learn to play it. They've always been a kind of mystery to me, pianos . . . guitars.

RICK. Mystery? (*And* OZZIE *is trying, awkwardly, desperately.*)

OZZIE. I mean, what do you think? Do you ever have to think what your fingers should be doing? What I mean is do you ever have to say—I don't know what— "This finger goes there and this other one does—" I mean, "It's on *this* ridge, now I chord all the strings and then switch it all." See? And do you have to tell yourself, "Now switch it all—first finger this ridge—second finger, down—third—somewhere." I mean, does that kind of thing ever happen? I mean, *How do you play it?* I keep having this notion of wanting some . . . thing . . . some material thing, and I've built it. And then there's this feeling I'm of value, that I'm on my way—I mean, moving—and I'm going to come to something eventually, some kind of acheivement. All this feelings of a child . . . in me . . . they shoot through me and then they're gone and they're not anything . . . anymore. But it's . . . a . . . wall . . . that I want . . . I think. I see myself doing it sometimes . . . all brick and stone . . . coils of steel. And then I finish . . . and the success of it is monumental and people come from far . . . to see . . . to look. They applaud. Ricky . . . teach me . . .

RICK. Ahhh . . . what, Dad?

OZZIE. Guitar, guitar.

RICK. Oh; sure. First you start with the basic "C" chord. You put the first finger on the second string . . .

OZZIE. But that's what I'm talking about. You don't do that. I know you don't.

RICK. (*Thinking he has misunderstood.*) Oh.

OZZIE. You just pick it up and play it. I don't have time for all that you're saying. That's what I've been telling you.

RICK. Well, maybe some other day then. Maybe Mom'll wanna learn, too. (*On his way for the door: all this dialogue, rapid, over-lapping.*)

OZZIE. No, no.

RICK. Just me and you then.

OZZIE. Right. Me and you.

RICK. I'll see you later.

OZZIE. What?

RICK. Maybe tomorrow.

OZZIE. No.

RICK. Well, maybe the next day then. (*And he is gone out the door.*)

OZZIE. NOW! NOW! (*And the door slams shut.*) I grew too old too quick. (*He turns to the audience.*) It was just a town I thought and no one remained to test me. I didn't even know it was leaving I was doing. I thought I'd go away and come back. Not leave. (*And he looks up at* DAVID's *room.*) YOU SONOFABITCH, (*And he is running up to* DAVID's *room.*) NOT LEAVE! (*And he bursts into* DAVID's *room. Silence.*) Restless, Dave; restless. Got a lot on my mind. Some of us can't just lay around, you know. You said I left that town like I was wrong, but I was right. A man proved himself out there, tested himself. So I went and then I ended up in the goddamn depression, what about that? I stood in goddamn lines of people begging bread and soup. You're not the only one who's had troubles. All of us, by God, David, think about that a little. (*Stepping out the door, slamming it.*) Just give somebody beside yourself some goddamn thought for a change. (*He now talks to the audience; they are his friends.*) Lived in goddamn dirty fields, made tents of our coats. Again and again . . . the whole of the length of this country, soot in our fingers, riding the rails . . . , a bum, hobo but young. And then one day . . . the brakeman, sees me hunched down in that railroad car and he orders me off. He stands distant, ordering that I jump . . . ! I don't understand and then he stops speaking . . . and . . . when he speaks again, pain is in his eyes and voice— "You're a runner," he says, "Christ, I didn't know you were a runner." And he moves to embrace me and with both hands lifts me high above his head—holds me there trembling, then flings me far out and I fall, I roll. All in the air, then slam down breathless, raw from the cinders . . . bruised and dizzy at the outskirts of this town, and I'm here, gone from that other town. I'm here. I make friends. We have good times even though things are rough. We point young girls out on the street. How good it feels to touch them. I start thinking of their bodies, having dreams of horses, breasts and crotches. And then one day the feeling is in me that I must see a train go by and I'll get on it or I won't, something will happen, but halfway down to where I was thrown off, I see how the grass in among the ties is tall, the rails rusted . . . Grass grows in abundance. No trains any longer come that way; they all go some other way . . . and far behind me, I turn to see Harriet young and lovely weaving among the weeds. I feel the wonder of her body moving toward me. She's the thing I think I'll enter to find my future . . . "Yes," I yell, "Sonofabitch! Bring her here. C'mon!" Swollen with pride, screaming and yelling, I stand there: "I'm ready. I'm ready . . . I'm ready." (*He has come down the stairs: he stands, arms spread, yelling.*)

BLACKOUT

(*MUSIC. LIGHTS SLOWLY UP.* Ozzie *sleeps on the couch.* Rick *sits in a chair, looking at his guitar. The girl,* Zung, *is in* David's *room. She sits on the bed behind* David, *who is slouched in a chair.* Harriet *enters dressed in a blue robe. She comes down the upstairs hallway.*)

Harriet. Have you seen my crossword puzzle book?
Rick. In the bathroom, Mom.
Harriet. Bathroom . . . ? Did I leave it there? (*Turning, heading back up the stairs.*)

RICK. Guess so, Mom. (*As* DAVID *sits abruptly up in his bed as if at a sudden, frightening sound.*)

DAVID. Who's there? There's someone there? (RICK *looks up;* DAVID *is standing, poking the air with his cane.*) Who's there? (*He opens the door to his room.*)

RICK. What'samatter? It's just me and Dad and Dad's sleeping.

DAVID. Sleeping? Is he?

RICK. On the davenport. You want me to wake him?

DAVID. Nooo . . . nooo. (*Moving swiftly, to descend to the living room.*)

RICK. Hey, could I get some pictures, Dave? Would you mind?

DAVID. Of course not. No.

RICK. (*Dashing off up the stairs while* DAVID *gropes to find the couch.*) Let me just go get some film and some flashes, okay?

DAVID. (*Standing behind the couch on which* OZZIE *sleeps,* DAVID *is looking after* RICK.) Sure.

OZZIE. Pardon? Par . . . don?

DAVID. (*Whispering into the ear of his father.*) I think you should know I've begun to hate you. I don't think you can tell me any more. If I had been an orphan with no one to count on me, I would have stayed there. Now . . . she is everywhere I look. (OZZIE *stirs.*) You think us good, we steal all you have.

OZZIE. Good . . . ole . . .

DAVID. No, no.

OZZIE. . . . nooo . . . nooooooo. . . .

DAVID. She would tell me you would not like her—she would touch her fingers to her eyes, and she knew how I must feel sometimes as you do.

OZZIE. ohhh, noooo . . . sleeping . . .

DAVID. You must hear me. It is only fraud that keeps us sane, I swear it.

OZZIE. David, sleeping . . . ! Oh, oh . . .

DAVID. It is not innocence I have lost! What is it I have lost?

OZZIE. Oh . . . , oh . . . (*As* RICK *has appeared high in the hallway where he hesitates.*)

DAVID. Don't you know? Do you see her in your sleep?

RICK. (*Hurrying down.*) I meant to get some good shots at the party, but I never got a chance the way things turned out. You can stay right there.

DAVID. (*Moving toward the chair on which rests* RICK's *guitar.*) I'll sit, all right? (RICK *rushes to save the guitar.*)

RICK. Sure. How you feelin', anyway, Dave? I mean, honest ta God, I'm hopin' you get better. Everybody is. I mean . . . (*He takes a picture.*) . . . you're not gonna go talkin' anymore crazy like about that guitar and all that, are you? You know what I mean. Not to Mom and Dad anyway. It scares 'em and then I get scared and I don't like it, okay? (*He moves on, taking more pictures.*)

DAVID. Sure. That guitar business wasn't serious, anyway, Rick. None of that. It was all just a little joke I felt like playing, a kind of little game. I was only trying to show you how I hate you.

RICK. Huh? (*Stunned,* RICKY *stares.*)

DAVID. To see you die is why I live, Rick.

RICK. Oh.

HARRIET. (*Appearing from off upstairs, the crossword puzzle book is her hands.*) Goodness gracious, Ricky, it was just where you said it would be, though I'm sure I don't know how it got there because I din't put it there. Hello, David.

DAVID. Hello.

OZZIE. OHHHHHHHHHHHHHHHH! (*Screaming, he comes awake, falling off the couch.*) Oh, boy, what a dream! Oh . . . (*Trying to get to his feet, but collapsing.*) Ohhhhhhh! God, leg's asleep. Jesus! (*And he flops about, sits there, rubbing his leg.*) Ohhhh, everybody. Scared hell out of me, that dream. I hollered. Did you hear me? And my leg's asleep, too. (*He hits the leg, stomps the floor.* HARRIET *sits on the couch, working her crossword puzzle book.* RICK, *slumped in a chair, reads a comic.* DAVID, *though, leans forward in his chair. He*

wants to know the effect of his whispering on his father.)
Did anybody hear me holler?

HARRIET. Not me.

RICK. What did you dream about, Dad?

OZZIE. I don't remember, but it was awful. (*Stomping the foot.*) Ohhhh, wake up, wake up. Hank was in it, though. And Dave. They stood over me, whispering,— I could feel how they hated me.

RICK. That really happened; he really did that, Dad.

OZZIE. Who did?

RICK. What you said.

OZZIE. No. No, I was sleeping. It scared me awful in my sleep. I'm still scared, honest to God, it was so awful.

DAVID. It's that sleeping in funny positions, Dad. It's that sleeping in some place that's not a bed.

OZZIE. Pardon?

DAVID. Makes you dream funny. What did Hank look like?

HARRIET. Ozzie, how do you spell "Apollo"?

OZZIE. What? I don't know.

RICK. Jesus, Dad, Schroeder got three home runs, you hear about that? Two in the second of the first and one in the third of the second. Goddamn, if he don't make MVP in the National, I'll eat my socks. You hear about that, Dad?

OZZIE. Yes, I did. Yes.

RICK. He's somethin'.

OZZIE. A pro.

HARRIET. Ozzie, can you think of a four letter word that starts with "G" and ends with "B"?

RICK. Glub.

HARRIET. Glub?

OZZIE. (*Almost simultaneously.*) Glub?

RICK. It's a cartoon word. Cartoon people say it when they're drowning. G-L-U-B.

OZZIE. (*On his feet now.*) Ricky. Ricky, I was wondering . . . when I was sleeping, were my eyes open? Was I seeing?

RICK. I didn't notice, Dad.

HARRIET. "Glub" doesn't work, Rick.

RICK. Try GRUB. That's what sourdoughs call their food. It's G-R—

OZZIE. WAIT A MINUTE!

RICK. G-R—

OZZIE. ALL OF YOU WAIT A MINUTE! LISTEN! Listen. I mean, I look for explanations. I look inside myself. For an explanation. I mean, I look inside *my* self. As I would look into water or the sky . . . the ocean. They're silver. Answers . . . silver and elusive . . . like fish. But if you can catch them in the sea . . . hook them as they flash by, snatch them up . . . , drag them down like birds from the sky . . . against all their struggle . . . when you're adrift and starving . . . they . . . can help you live. (*He falters; he stands among them, straining to go further, searching for some sign of comprehension in their faces.*)

RICK. Mom, Dad's hungry . . . I think. He wants some fish, I—

OZZIE. SHUT UP!

RICK. (*Hurt deeply.*) Dad?

OZZIE. PIECE OF SHIT! SHUT UP! SHUT UP!

HARRIET. Ozzie . . . !

OZZIE. (*Roaring down at* DAVID.) I don't want to hear about her. I'm not interested in her. You did what you did and I was no part of it. You understand me? I don't want to hear anymore about her! Look at him. Sitting there. Listening. I'm tired of hearing you, Dave. You understand that? I'm tired of hearing you and your cry-baby voice and your cry-baby stories. And your cry-baby slobbering and your— (*And his voice is possessed with astonished loathing.*) LOOK . . . AT . . . HIM! YOU MAKE ME WANT TO VOMIT! HARRIET! YOU— (*And he whirls on* HARRIET.) YOU! Your internal organs —your internal female organs—they've got some kind of poison in them. They're backing up some kind of rot into the world. I think you ought to have them cut out of you. I MEAN, I JUST CAN'T STOP THINKING

ABOUT IT. I JUST CAN'T STOP THINKING
ABOUT IT. LITTLE BITTY CHINKY KIDS HE
WANTED TO HAVE! LITTLE BITTY CHINKY
YELLOW KIDS! DIDN'T YOU! FOR OUR GRAND-
CHILDREN! (*And he slaps* DAVID *with one hand.*)
LITTLE BITTY YELLOW PUFFY— (*He breaks, grop-
ing for the word.*) . . . creatures . . . ! FOR OUR
GRANDCHILDREN! (*He slaps* DAVID *again, again.*)
THAT'S ALL YOU CARED! (DAVID, *a howl in his
throat, has stood up.*)

HARRIET. Ohhh, Ozzie, God forgive you the cruelty of
your words. All children are God's children.

(DAVID *is standing rigidly and the downstairs front door
blows open, and in fierce and sudden light above
him, the girl,* ZUNG, *steps forward to the edge of
his room as he is looking up at her.*)

DAVID. I didn't know you were here. I didn't know. I
will buy you clothing. I have lived with them all my life.
I will make them not hate you. I will buy you boots.
(*And he is moving toward her, climbing the stairs.*) They
will see you. The seasons will amaze you. Texas is enor-
mous. Ohio is sometimes green. There will be time. We
will learn to speak. And it will be as it was in that moment when we looked in the dark and our eyes were
tongues that could speak and the hurting . . . all of it
. . . stopped, and there was total understanding in you
of me and in me of you . . . and . . . (*Near her now,
stepping into his room through the wall, he reaches in
a tentative way toward her.*) such delight in your eyes
that I felt it, (*And she has begun to move away from
him.*) yet . . . I. (*And she is moving away and down.*)
discarded you. I discarded you. Forgive me. You moved
to leave as if you were struggling not to move, not to
leave. "She's the thing most possibly of value in my life,"
I said. "She is garbage and filth and I must get her back
if I wish to live. Sickness, I must cherish her." Zung,

there were old voices inside me I had trusted all my life as if they were my own. I didn't know I shouldn't hear them. So reasonable and calm they seemed a source of wisdom. "She's all of everything impossible made possible, cast her down," they said. "Go home." And I did as they told; and now I know that I am not awake but asleep, and in my sleep . . . there is nothing . . . (*And* ZUNG, *having descended the stairs is now before the open door. She stands facing it, about to leave.*) . . . nothing . . . ! What do you want from me to make you stay? (*And it is almost as if he snaps out of a dream to see her.*) I'll do it. I'll do what you want!

RICK. (*In the dark before his father, camera in hand.*) Lookee here, Dad. Cheer up! Cheer up!

DAVID. Nooooo. . . . (*As* ZUNG *turns to look up at him. And* RICK *takes the picture; there is the flash.*) NOOOOOOOOOOOOOOO! STAAAAAAY! (*And the door slams shut, leaving* ZUNG *inside. A slide of* OZZIE *appears on the screen, a close-up, his pained and puzzled face. Music, a falling of notes. The lights are going to black. Perhaps "Intermission" is on the bottom of the slide. The slide blinks out.*)

END OF ACT ONE

ACT TWO

Blackness.

Slide: Close-up of man, ruddy, smiling round face. Color photo.

CHILD I. Who's zat?
FEMALE ADULT. I don't know.
MALE ADULT. Looks like a neighbor.
FEMALE ADULT. How can you say it's a neighbor? You don't know. (*New slide appears: scenery, color.*)
CHILD 2. Oh, that's a pretty one. (*New slide, color:* FATHER DONALD *in a boxing pose.*)
CHILD. Oh, lookee that.
MALE ADULT. Father what's-his-name. You know.

(*Another slide: of* FATHER DONALD, *slightly different boxing pose.*)

FEMALE ADULT. There he is again.
CHILD 2. Wow.

(*LIGHTS UP on the downstairs and* OZZIE *and* HARRIET *are then with* FATHER DONALD, *a slightly rotund, serious man.* DAVID *is in his room on his bed.* HARRIET *sits on the couch,* FATHER DONALD *is on a chair.* OZZIE *is in the chair beside him. We have the feeling they have been there a long, long time.*)

FATHER DONALD. I deal with people and their uneasiness on a regular basis, all the time, you see. Everybody I talk to is nervous . . . one way or another . . . so . . . I anticipate no real trouble in dealing with Dave.

51

You have no idea the things people do and then tell me
once that confessional door is shut, I'm looking forward
actually, to speaking with him. Religion has been slough-
ing off a lot lately, but I think there's a relevancy much
larger than the credit most give. We're growing—and
our insights, when we have them, are two-fold. I for one
have come recently to understand how very often what
seems a spiritual problem is in fact a problem of the mind
rather than the spirit—not that the two can in fact be
separated, though, in theory, they very often are. So
what we must do is apply these theories to fact. At which
point we would find that mind and spirit are one and I, a
priest, am a psychiatrist, and psychiatrists are priests. I
mean— I feel like I'm rambling— Am I rambling?

HARRIET. Oh, no, Father.

OZZIE. Nooo . . . noo.

HARRIET. Father, this is hard for me to say, but I . . .
feel . . . his problem is he sinned against the sixth com-
mandment with whores.

FATHER DONALD. That's very likely over there.

HARRIET. And then the threat of death each day made
it so much worse.

FATHER DONALD. I got the impression from our earlier
talk he'd had a relationship of some duration.

HARRIET. A day or two, wouldn't you say, Ozzie.

OZZIE. (*Distracted oddly preoccupied with his chair.*)
A three-day pass I'd say . . . though I don't know, of
course.

FATHER DONALD. They're doing a lot of psychiatric
studies on that phenomenon right now, did you know
that? (*And the door pops open, in bounds* RICK.)

HARRIET. Oh, Rick . . . !

RICK. Hi, Mom; hi, Dad.

OZZIE. Hi, Rick.

FATHER DONALD. Rick, Hello! (*Rising.*)

RICK. Oh, Father Donald . . . Hi. (*No time for*
FATHER DONALD, RICK'S *speeding for the kitchen.*)

OZZIE. Look at him heading for the fudge.

FATHER DONALD. Well, he's a good big strong sturdy boy.

RICK. Hungry and thirsty.

FATHER DONALD. And don't you ever feel bad about it, either! (*He stands for an instant a little uncertain what to do.*) Dave's up in his room, I imagine, so maybe I'll just head on up and have my little chat. He is why I'm here, after all.

HARRIET. Fine.

OZZIE. (*Still distracted. He stares at the chair in which* FATHER DONALD *was sitting.*) First door top of the stairs.

FATHER DONALD. And could I use the bathroom, please, before I see ole Dave? Got to see a man about a horse.

HARRIET. Oh, Father, certainly: it's just down the hall. Fifth door.

OZZIE. (*Nearing the chair.*) What's wrong with that chair?

HARRIET. It's the blue door, Father!

OZZIE. I don't like that chair. I think it's stupid . . . looking . . . (*As* RICK *enters from the kitchen, eating fudge.*) Ricky, sit. Sit in that chair.

RICK. What . . . ?

OZZIE. Go on, sit, sit. (RICK *hurries to the chair, sits, eats.* OZZIE *is fixated on the chair.*)

HARRIET. Oh, Ricky, take your father's picture, he looks so silly.

OZZIE. I just don't think that chair is any good. I just don't think it's comfortable. Father Donald looked ill at ease all the while he was sitting there.

HARRIET. Well, he had to go to the bathroom, Ozzie, what do you expect?

OZZIE. (*To* RICKY.) Get up. It's just not right. (OZZIE *flops into the chair. He sits. He fidgets.*) Noooooo. It's just not a comfortable chair at all, I don't know why. (*He rises: on the move toward the couch.*) I don't like it. How much did we pay?

HARRIET. What do you think you're doing?

OZZIE. And this couch isn't comfortable either.

HARRIET. It's a lovely couch.

OZZIE. (*He tests.*) But it isn't comfortable. Nooooo. And I'm not really sure it's lovely, either. Did we pay two hundred dollars?

HARRIET. What? Oh, more.

OZZIE. How much?

HARRIET. I don't know, I told you.

OZZIE. You don't. I don't. It's gone anyway, isn't it?

HARRIET. Ozzie, what does it matter?

OZZIE. (*Already on the move for the stairs.*) I'm going upstairs. I'll be upstairs.

HARRIET. Wait a minute. (*As he keeps moving.*) I want to talk to you. *I think we ought to talk! (Emotion well beneath her voice stops him, turns him.*) I mean, it's nothing to worry about or anything, but you don't know about it and it's your house, you're involved—so it's just something I mention. You're the man of the house, you ought to know. The police were here . . . earlier today.

OZZIE. What? OH, my god.

HARRIET. The police. Two of them. Two. A big and a small—they— (*He is dazed; he does not know whether to go up or down, listen or leave. He nods.*) It was just a little bit ago; not long at all.

OZZIE. Jesus Christ. (*He decends.*)

HARRIET. Oh, I know, I know. Just out of the blue like that—it's how I felt, too. I did, I did.

OZZIE. *What—police?*

HARRIET. It was when you were gone for groceries. I mean, they thought they were supposed to be here. We wanted it, they thought.

OZZIE. No, no.

HARRIET. Somebody called them to come here. They thought it had been us. They were supposed to look through David's luggage, they thought.

OZZIE. They—were—what?

HARRIET. That's what I mean. That's exactly what I—

OZZIE. *Look through his luggage? There's nothing wrong with his luggage!*

HARRIET. Isn't it incredible? Somebody called them—they didn't know who—no name was given and it sounded muffled through a handkerchief, they said. I said, "Well, it wasn't us." Told them, "Don't you worry; we're all all right here." It must have been a little joke by somebody.

OZZIE. What about Dave?

HARRIET. No, no.

OZZIE. Or Ricky? Did you ask Ricky?

HARRIET. Ricky?

OZZIE. Ricky! Ricky!

RICK. (*Popping in from the kitchen, thinking he was called.*) What's up, Dad?

OZZIE. I DON'T KNOW.

RICK. I thought you called. (*Popping back out into the kitchen.*)

OZZIE. (*To* HARRIET.) You ask him; you ask him. I think the whole thing's preposterous—absolutely—

HARRIET. (*As* RICKY, *re-emerges to look and listen.*) Ricky, do you know anything about anybody calling the police to come here?

OZZIE. (*Turning and moving for the stairs.*) I'm going upstairs. I'll be upstairs.

RICK. The police? (*As she is turning to look and half-step after* OZZIE.) Oh, no, Mom, not me. Okay if I use the car?

HARRIET. What?

FATHER DONALD. (*Encountering* OZZIE *in the upstairs hallway.*) Gonna take care of old Dave right now.

OZZIE. I'm going upstairs. I'll be upstairs. (*Exiting as* HARRIET *is looking up at them.*)

RICK. Bye, Mom.

HARRIET. What? Oh. (*Looking back as* RICK *is out the door.*) BE CAREFUL!

FATHER DONALD. (*After a slight hesitation.*) Ozzie said to tell you he was going upstairs,

HARRIET. What?

FATHER DONALD. Ozzie said to tell you he was going upstairs.

HARRIET. (*She stares at him a moment.*) Oh, Father, I'm so glad you're here. (*And she exits into the kitchen, leaving* FATHER DONALD. *He nods, knocks on* DAVE'S *door.*)

FATHER DONALD. Dave? (*He opens the door, eases into the semi-dark of the room.*) Dave? It's me . . . , Dave. . . . (*Finding a light, he flicks it on.*) Ohh, Dave, golly, you look just fine. Here I expected to see you all worn out and there you are looking so good. It's me, Dave, Father Donald. Let me shake your hand. (DAVID'S *raising hand comes up far off from* FATHER DONALD. *The priest, his own hand extended, has to move nearly around the bed before he can shake* DAVID'S *hand.*) No, no, David. Here. Over here. Can't see me, can you. There you go. Yes, Sir, let me tell you, I'm proud. A lot of people might tell you that, I know, but I mean it, and I'll stand behind it if there's anything I can do for you— anything at all.

DAVID. No. I'm all right.

FATHER DONALD. And that's the amazing part of it, Dave, you are. You truly are. It's plain as day. Gollee, I just don't know how to tell you how glad I am to see you in such high fine spirits. Would you like my blessing? (*He gets to his feet.*) Let me just give you my blessing and then we'll talk things over a little and— (DAVID'S *slashing cane strikes into the hand moving into the position to bless.*) Ohhhhhhhhhhhhhh! (*Wincing: teeth gritted.*) Oh, Dave; oh, watch out what you're doing!

DAVID. I know.

FATHER DONALD. No, no, I mean, you swung it in the air, you—hit me.

DAVID. Yes.

FATHER DONALD. No, no, you don't understand, you—

DAVID. I was trying to hit you, Father.

(FATHER DONALD *stares, taking this in.*)

FATHER DONALD. What?

DAVID. I didn't send for you.

FATHER DONALD. I know, I know, your poor mother—your poor mother—

DAVID. I don't want you here, Father; get out!

FATHER DONALD. David!

DAVID. Get out, I'm sick of you. You've been in one Goddamn corner or another of this room all my life making signs at me, whispering, wanting to splash me with water or mark me with oil—some Goddamn hocus-pocus. I feel reverence for the air and the air is empty, Father. Now get the fuck out of here.

FATHER DONALD. No, no, no, no, David. No, no. I can't give that to you. You'll have to get that from somewhere else.

DAVID. I don't want anything from you!

FATHER DONALD. I'm supposed to react now in some foolish way—I see—some foolish, foolish way that will discredit me—isn't that right. Oh, of course it is. It's an excuse to dismiss my voice that you're seeking, an excuse for the self-destruction your anger has made you think you want, and I'm supposed to give it. I'm supposed to find all this you're doing obscene and sacrilegious instead of seeing it as the gesture of true despair that it is. You're trying to make me disappear, but it's not going to happen. No, no. No such luck, David. I understand you, you see. Everything about you.

DAVID. Do you?

FATHER DONALD. The way you're troubled.

DAVID. I didn't know that, Father.

FATHER DONALD. You say that sarcastically— "Do you? I didn't know that." As if to imply you're so complicated I couldn't ever understand you when I already have. You see, I've been looking into a few things, David, giving some things some thought. I have in my hand a magazine—you can't see it, I know—but it's there. A psychiatric journal in which there is an article of some interest and it deals with soldiers and some of them carried on as you did and then there's some others who didn't. It's not all just a matter of hocus-pocus any longer.

DAVID. Carried . . . on . . . Father?

FATHER DONALD. That whore. That yellow whore. You understand. You knew I was bringing the truth when I came which is why you hit me.

DAVID. I thought you didn't even know the problem. You came in here all bubbly and jolly asking how did I feel.

FATHER DONALD. That was only a little ruse, David; a little maneuver to put you off your guard. I only did that to mislead you. That's right. Your mother gave me all the basics some weeks ago and I filled in the rest from what I know. You see, if it's a fight you want, it's what you'll get. Your soul is worth some time and sweat from me. You're valued by others, David, even if you don't value yourself. (*He produces a magazine; the cover is colorful. He waves it in the air.*) It's all here—right here—in these pages. It was demonstrated beyond any possible doubt that people—soldiers—who are compelled for some reason not even they themselves understand to establish personal-sexual relationships with whores are inferior to those who don't; they're maladjusted, embittered, non-goal-oriented misfits. The sexual acceptance of another person, David, is intimate and extreme; this kind of acceptance of an alien race is in fact the rejection of one's own race—it is in fact the rejection of one's own self—it is sickness, David. Now I'm a religious man, a man of the spirit, but knowledge is knowledge and I must accept what is proven fact whether that fact come from science or philosophy or whatever. What kind of man are you that you think you can deny it? You're in despair, David, whether you think of it that way or not. It's only into a valley of ruin that you are trying to lock yourself. You can only die there, David.

Accept me. Let God open your eyes; let Him. He will
redeem you. Not I nor anyone, but only Him—yet if
you reject me, you reject Him. My hand is His. His
blessing. (*The hand is raising as if the very words elevate
it.*) My blessing. Let me give you my blessing. (*And
DAVID's cane hits like a snake. FATHER DONALD cries
out as if he had forgotten.*) Let . . . me . . . bless
you! (*The hand is raising: he will try again.*) Please . . .
(DAVID, *striking again, stands. He hits again and again.*)
David! David! (FATHER DONALD *is terrified.*) Stop it.
Let me bless you. (DAVID *hits the arm; he hits* FATHER
DONALD's *leg.*)

DAVID. I don't want you here!

FATHER DONALD. You don't know what you're saying.
(*But now the blow seems about to come straight down
on his head. He yells and covers his head with his arms.
The blow hits. He picks up a chair, holds it up for pro-
tection.*) Stop it. Stop it, Goddamnit, Stop hitting me.
Stop it. You are in despair. (*He slams the chair down.*)
A man who hits a priest is in despair! (*Whistling, the
cane slams into his arm.*) Ohhhhh, this pain—this terrible
pain in my arm—I offer it to earn you your salvation.

DAVID. Get out!

FATHER DONALD. Death! Do you understand that.
Death. Death is your choice. You are in despair. (*Turning to leave.*)

DAVID. And may God reward *you*, Father.

FATHER DONALD. (*Turning back as* DAVID *flops down
on the bed.*) Oh yes; yes of course, you're so confident
now, young and strong. Look at you; full of spunk; smiling. But all that'll change. Your tune'll change in time.
What about pain, Dave? Physical pain. What do you do
when it comes? Now you send me away, but in a little
while you'll call me back, run down by time, lying with
death on your bed . . . in an empty house . . . gagging
on your own spit you cannot swallow; you'll call me
then, nothing left to you but fear and Christ's black
judging eyes about to find and damn you, you'll call.

DAVID. That's not impossible, Father.

FATHER DONALD. I don't even like you; do you know that? I DON'T EVEN LIKE YOU!

DAVID. Tell them I hit you when you go down.

FATHER DONALD. (*Near the door, thinking about trying to bless from there.*) No. No, they've pain enough already.

DAVID. Have they? You get the fuck out of here before I kill you. (*As it he has read* FATHER DONALD'S *mind and knows what the man is thinking,* DAVID'S *cane is rising ready to strike.*)

FATHER DONALD. (*Moving not a muscle.*) THOUGH I DO NOT MOVE MY HAND, I BLESS YOU! YOU ARE BLESSED! (*And he exits hurriedly, heading straight down the hall toward the bathroom. LIGHTS UP downstairs: it seems a lovely afternoon as* RICK *and* HARRIET *enter from the kitchen, chatting.*)

HARRIET. So the thing I want to do—I just think it would be so nice if we could get Dave a date with some nice girl.

RICK. Oh, sure.

HARRIET. Do you think that would be a good idea?

(OZZIE *descending from the attic, pauses to peek into* DAVID'S *room; he finds* DAVID *asleep and, after a moment, continues on down.*)

RICK. Sure.

HARRIET. Do you know any girls you think might get along with David?

RICK. No, but I still think it's really a good idea and I'll keep it in mind for all the girls I meet and maybe I'll meet one. Here comes Dad. Hi, Dad. Bye, Mom.

HARRIET. Oh, Ozzie, did you see what they were doing?

OZZIE. Dave's sleeping, Harriet; Father Donald's gone.

HARRIET. What? He can't be gone.

OZZIE. I thought maybe he was down here. How about the kitchen?

HARRIET. No, no, I just came out of the kitchen. Where were you upstairs? Are you sure he wasn't in David's room?

OZZIE. I was in the attic.

HARRIET. Well, maybe he saw the light and came up to join you and you missed each other on the way up and down. Why don't you go check?

OZZIE. I turned off all the lights, Harriet. The attic's dark now.

HARRIET. Well, yell up anyway—

OZZIE. But that attic's dark now, Harriet.

HARRIET. Just in case.

OZZIE. What are you trying to say?—Father Donald's up in the attic in the dark? I mean, if he was up there and I turned off the lights, he'd have said something— "Hey, I'm here," or something. It's stupid to think he wouldn't (*And he sits down.*)

HARRIET. No more stupid to think that than to think he'd leave without telling us what happened with David.

OZZIE. All right, all right. (*Storming to the base of the stairs.*) HEEEEEEYYYYYYYYYYYYYY! UP THERE-EEEEE! ANYBODY UP THERE? (*As there is a brief silence, he turns toward* HARRIET.)

DAVID. WHAT'S THAT, DAD? (*In his bed in his room.*)

OZZIE. (*He falters, looks about.*) What?

DAVID. WHAT'S UP, DAD?

OZZIE. OH, DAVE, NO, NOT YOU.

DAVID. WHY ARE YOU YELLING?

OZZIE. NO, NO, WE JUST THOUGHT FATHER DONALD WAS UP THERE IN THE ATTIC, DAVE. DON'T YOU WORRY ABOUT IT.

DAVID. I'M THE ONLY ONE UP HERE, DAD!

OZZIE. BUT . . . YOU'RE NOT IN THE ATTIC, SEE?

DAVID. I'M IN MY ROOM.

OZZIE. I KNOW YOU'RE IN YOUR ROOM.

DAVID. YOU WANT ME TO GO UP IN THE ATTIC?

OZZIE. NO! GODDAMNIT, JUST—

DAVID. I DON'T KNOW WHAT YOU WANT.

OZZIE. I WANT YOU TO SHUT UP, DAVE, THAT'S WHAT I WANT, JUST—

FATHER DONALD. (*Appearing from off upstairs.*) What's the matter? What's all the yelling?

HARRIET. Oh, Father!

OZZIE. Father, hello, hello.

HARRIET. How did it go? Did it go all right?

FATHER DONALD. Fine, just fine. (*Coming down the steps. He seems as if nothing out of the ordinary has happened.*)

HARRIET. Oh, you're perspiring so, though—look at you.

FATHER DONALD. Well, I've got a lot on my mind. It happens. Nerves. I've other appointments. Many, many. (*All this as he is manuevering for the door.*)

HARRIET. You mean you're leaving? What are you saying?

FATHER DONALD. I must.

HARRIET. But we've got to talk.

FATHER DONALD. Call me.

HARRIET. Father . . . bless me . . . !

FATHER DONALD. What . . . ?

HARRIET. Bless me . . .

FATHER DONALD. Of course.

(*And she bows her head. And* OZZIE, *seeing them, is startled, and the* PRIEST *blesses them murmuring the Latin.*)

HARRIET. Ohhh, Father, thank you so much. (*Touching his hand.*) Shall I walk you to your car?

FATHER DONALD. Fine, fine. That's all right. Sure. (*Backing for the door.*)

OZZIE. (*Nodding.*) DAVE, SAY "GOODBYE" TO
FATHER DONALD, HE'S LEAVING NOW.
FATHER DONALD. GOODBYE, DAVE!
DAVID. GOODBYE, FATHER!

(*BLACKOUT as* HARRIET *and* FATHER DONALD *are
going out the door. MUSIC. And* OZZIE *having taken
a moment to think is discovered in late night light,
climbing the stairs to* DAVID'S *door, where, after
hesitating an instant,* OZZIE *gently knocks.*)

OZZIE. Dave, I'd like to come in . . . , if I could.
(*Easing in.*) Awful dark; can I put on a light? (*Silence.*)
I mean, we don't need one; not really. I just thought
we might . . . I mean, first of all, I want to apologize for
the way I hit you the other day, I don't know why I did
it. I'm . . . gonna sit down here on the edge of the bed.
Are you awake enough to understand? I am your father,
you know, and I could command . . . if I wanted. I
don't; but I could. I'm going to sit. (*Slight pause.*) I
mean, it's so sad the way you just go on and on . . .
and I'd like to have time for you, but you want so much;
I have important things, too. I have plans; I'm older,
you know; if I fail to fulfill them, who will do it: Not
you, though you could. And Rick's too busy. Do you
understand? There's no evidence in the world of me no
sign or trace as if everything I've ever done were no
more than smoke. My life has closed behind me like
water. But I must not care about it. I must not. Though
I have inside me a kind of grandeur I can't realize, many
things and memories of a darker time when we were very
different—harder—nearer to the air and we thought of
nothing as a gift. But I can't make you see that. There's
no way. It's what I am, but it's not what you are. Even
if I had the guitar, I would only stand here telling my
fingers what to do, but they would do nothing. You
would not see . . . I can't get beyond these hands. I
jamb in the fingers. I break on the bone. I am . . . lonely.

I mean, oh, no, not exactly lonely, not really. That's a little strong, actually. . . . (*Silence.*) I mean . . . Dave . . . (*And he pulls from his back pocket* DAVID's *overseas cap.*) What's this?

DAVID. What?

OZZIE. This cap. What is it? I cut myself on it. I was rummaging in your stuff upstairs, your bags and stuff and I grabbed it. It cut me. (*As* DAVID *is reaching for the cap.*)

DAVID. Oh . . . yes.

OZZIE. There are razors sewn into it. Why is that?

DAVID. To cut people. (*Slowly putting the cap on his head.*)

OZZIE. Oh.

DAVID. Here . . . , I'll show you. . . . (*Getting slowly to his feet.*) You're on the street, see. You walk . . . and see someone who's after you—you wait . . . (*He tenses. His hand rises to the tip of the cap.*) . . . as they get near . . . slowly you remove the hat—they think you're going to toss it aside, see? You . . . *snap it! You snap it!* (*Seizing the front edge of the cap between thumb and finger, he snaps it down. It whistles past* OZZIE, *who jumps.*) It cuts them. They hold their face. However you want them, they're yours. You can stomp them, kick them. This is on the street. I'd like to do that to somebody, wouldn't you?

OZZIE. Huh?

DAVID. It'd be fun.

OZZIE. Oh, sure. I . . .

DAVID. Who told you to buy this house?

OZZIE. It's a good house. Solid. Not one of those prefabs, those—

DAVID. It's a coffin. You made it big so you wouldn't know, but that's what it is, and not all the curtains and pictures and lamps in the world can change it. He threw you off a fast free train, Ozzie.

OZZIE. I don't care.

DAVID. Do you know, Dad, it seemed sometimes I

would rise, and slam with my fists into the walls of a city. Pointing at buildings, I turned them into fire. I took the fleeing people into my fingers and bent them to touch their heads to their heels, each screaming at the sight of their brain turning black. And now sometimes I miss them, all those screaming people. I wish they were here with us, you and Mom and Rick and Zung and me. (*Pause.*)

OZZIE. Mom and Rick and who and you, Dave?

DAVID. Zung. (*The GIRL is moving nearer to them now.*)

OZZIE. Zung, Dave?

DAVID. She's here. They were all just hunks of meat that had no mind to know of me until I cared for her. It was simple. We lived in a house. She didn't want to come back here, Dad, she wanted me to stay there. And in all the time I knew her, she cost me six dollars that I had to sneak into her purse. Surprise? In time I'll show you some things. You'll see them. I will be your father. (*Tossing the cap at* OZZIE.)

OZZIE. Pardon, Dave? (*Shaken, struggling to catch the cap.*)

DAVID. What's wrong? You sound like something's terribly wrong?

OZZIE. No. No, no. I'm fine. Your poor mother—she's why I'm here. Your poor mother, sick with grief. She's mine to care for you know. It's me you're after, yet you torment her. No more. No more. That's what I came up here to tell you.

DAVID. (*Getting to his feet.*) Good.

OZZIE. You're phoney, David—phoney—trying to make up for the thousands you butchered, when if you were capable of love at all you would love us, your mother and me—not that we matter—

DAVID. (*Exiting the room.*) I know.

OZZIE. I want her happy.

DAVID. Of course.

(*As* Ozzie *follows a little into the hall and* David *is gone.* Harriet *enters slowly from the kitchen, sees* Ozzie, *then the room's open door.*)

Harriet. Did you have a nice talk?

Ozzie. (*Heading toward her.*) Harriet, what would you say if I said I wanted some checking done?

Harriet. I don't know what you mean. In what way do you mean?

Ozzie. Take a look at that. But just be careful.

Harriet. What is it?

Ozzie. His cap. There are razor blades sewn in it; all along the edge.

Harriet. Ozzie . . . , ohhh! Goodness.

Ozzie. That's what I mean. And I was reading just yesterday—some of them bring back guns and knives. Bombs. We've got somebody living in this house who's killed people, Harriet, and that's a fact we've got to face. I mean, I think we ought to do some checking. You know that test where they check teeth against old X-rays.

Harriet. Ohhh, my God . . . !

Ozzie. I know, I know, it scares me, too, but what are we talking about? We're talking about bombs and guns and knives and sometimes I don't even think it's David up there. I feel funny sometimes, I mean, and I want his fingerprints taken. I think we should have his blood-type—

Harriet. Oh, Ozzie, it was you.

Ozzie. Huh?

Harriet. You did it. It was you. You got this out of his luggage, all his baggage upstairs. You broke in and searched and called the police.

Ozzie. What?

Harriet. You told them to come here and then you lied and said you didn't.

Ozzie. What? No.

Harriet. You did and you lied and now you're lying again. What's wrong with you?

OZZIE. Oh, no. No.

HARRIET. What's happening to you? It's sick and disgusting—to call the police on your own son is sick and disgusting!

OZZIE. But I didn't do it. I didn't. (*As* DAVID *appears in the upstairs hallway, moving to return to his room.*) I didn't. No, no. And even if I did what would it mean but I changed my mind, that's all. Sure. (*Looking up at* DAVID *moving in the hall toward his room.*) I called and then changed my mind and said I didn't when I did and since when is there anything wrong in that? It would mean only that I have a little problem of ambivalence. I got a minor problem of ambiguity goin' for me here, is all, and you're exaggerating everything all out of proportion. You're distorting everything! All of you! (*And he whirls to leave.*) If I have to lie to live, I will! (*He runs.*)

HARRIET. Where are you going? (*He is running.*) Come back here, Ozzie. Where are you going? Where are you going?

OZZIE. Kitchen. Kitchen. (*As he gallops out of sight out the front door. BLACKOUT. MUSIC. LIGHTS UP. Bright afternoon.* HARRIET *is alone, dusting.* RICK, *carrying books, enters from the kitchen and heads for the stairs to go to his room.*)

HARRIET. One day, Ricky . . . , there were these two kittens and a puppy all in our backyard fighting. The kittens were little fur-balls, so angry, and the little puppy, yapping and yapping. I was just a girl, but I picked them up in my arms, I held them all in my arms and they got very, very quiet.

RICK. I'm going up to my bedroom and study my History and English and Trigonometry, Mom.

HARRIET. Do you know, I've called Father Donald seven times now—seven times and haven't got an answer. Isn't that funny? He's starting to act like Jesus. You never hear from him. Isn't that funny?

RICK. I'm going up to my bedroom and study my

History and English and Trigonometry, Mom, ok?

HARRIET. Fine, Ricky. Look in on David, would you?

RICK. Sure.

HARRIET. Goodnight.

RICK. (*Calling as he passes* DAVE'S *door.*) Hi, Dave.

DAVID. Hi, Rick.

RICK. DAVE'S OKAY, MOM. (*She is at the base of the stairs and he goes from view. She turns back to her work and the door opens and* OZZIE *enters.*)

OZZIE. Harriet! Can you guess what happened? You'll never guess what happened. (*She continues cleaning.*) Harriet, wait; stop.

HARRIET. Ozzie, I've got work to do.

OZZIE. But I want to tell you something.

HARRIET. All right, tell me; I can clean and listen; I can do both.

(*Rushing toward her as she moves away, he has the lapel of his jacket, the color stretched out in his fingers before him. She must see.*)

OZZIE. Lookit; look at that. What do you think that is? That spot on my coat, do you see it? That yellow?

HARRIET. (*Distressed; touching the spot.*) Ohhhh, Ozzie . . . !

OZZIE. And the red mark on my neck.

HARRIET. (*Wincing.*) Ohh, Ozzie, what happened? A bee sting! You got stung by a bee!

OZZIE. No, no; I was walking—thinking—trying to solve our problems. Somebody hit me with an egg. They threw it at me. I got hit with an egg. (*She stares, incredulous.*) That's right. I was just walking down the street and—bang—I was hit. I almost blacked out; I almost fell down.

HARRIET. Ozzie, my God, who would do such a thing?

OZZIE. I don't know. That's the whole point. I've racked my brain to understand and I can't. I was just walking along. That's all I was doing.

HARRIET. You mean you didn't even see them?

OZZIE. (*He is pacing, his excitment growing.*) They were in a car. I saw the car. And I saw the hand, too. Somebody's hand. A very large hand. Incredibly large.

HARRIET. What kind of car?

OZZIE. I don't know. An old one—black—big high fenders.

HARRIET. A Buick.

OZZIE. I think so; yes. Cruising up and down, up and down.

HARRIET. Was it near here? Why don't you sit down? (*Trying to help him sit, to calm and comfort him.*) Sit down. Relax. (*He obeys, hardly aware of what he is doing, sort of squating on the couch, his body rigid with tension, as the story obsesses him.*)

OZZIE. And I heard them, too. They were hollering.

HARRIET. What did they say?

OZZIE. I don't know. It was just all noise. I couldn't understand.

HARRIET. (*As if this realization doubles the horror.*) It was more than one? My God!

OZZIE. I don't know. Two at least, at the very least. One to drive and one to throw. Maybe even three. A lookout sort of, peering up and down and then he sees me; "There," he says; he points me out, I'm strolling along like a stupid ass, I don't even see them. The driver picks up speed. (*And now he is rising from the couch, reliving the story, cocking his arm.*) The thrower cocks his arm . . .

HARRIET. Ozzie, please, can't you relax? You look awful.

OZZIE. Nooo, I can't relax, Goddamnit! (*Off he goes, pacing again.*)

HARRIET. You look all flushed and sweating; please.

OZZIE. It just makes me so goddamn mad the more I think about it. It really does. GODDAMNIT! GODDAMNIT!

HARRIET. Oh, you poor thing.

OZZIE. Because it was calculated; it was calculated, Harriet, because that egg had been boiled to just the right point so it was hard enough to hurt but not so hard it wouldn't splatter. The filthy sonsabitches, but I'm gonna find 'em, I swear that to God, I'm gonna find 'em. I'm gonna kill 'em. I'm gonna cut out their hearts! (*As* RICK *appears at the top of the stairs.*)

RICK. —Hey! What's all the racket? What's—

OZZIE. Ricky, come down here!—Goddamn 'em—

HARRIET. Ricky, somebody hit your father with an egg!

RICK. Hit him? (*Descending hurriedly.*) Hit Dad? (*Worried.*)

OZZIE. They just threw it! Where's Dave? Dave here? (*He is suddenly looking around, moving for the stairs.*) I wana tell Dave. DAVE!

HARRIET. Ozzie, give me your jacket! (*She is following him, tugging at the jacket.*)

OZZIE. I wanna tell Dave! (*Struggling with* HARRIET *to get the jacket off.*)

HARRIET. I'll take the spot off.

OZZIE. I gotta tell ole Dave! (*And the jacket is in her arms, he races up the stairs.*) DAVE? DAVE! HEY, DAVE? (*But* DAVID *is not in his room. While* HARRIET *descends to the wall counter and drawers,* OZZIE *hurries off down the hallway. From a drawer* HARRIET *takes a spray container and begins to go about cleaning the jacket.*)

RICK. (*Wandering near to her.*) Boy, that's something, huh. What you got there, Mom?

HARRIET. (*As* RICK *watches.*) Meyer Spot Remover, do you know it? It gives just a sprinkling . . . like snow, which brushed away, leaves the fabric clean and fresh like spring.

(*As* OZZIE *and* DAVID *are rushing out from the hallway and down the stairs.* RICKY *moves to them to take a picture.*)

Ozzie. But it happened—and then there's this car tearin' off up the street, Christ Jesus, I said, I just been hit with an egg. Jesus Christ, that's impossible, and the way I felt—the way I feel—Harriet, let's have some beer; let's have some good beer for the boys and me. (*With a sigh, she moves to obey: she will bring beer; she will bring peanuts.* Ozzie *now is pleased with his high energy, with his being the center of attention.*) It took me back to when I was a kid. Ole Fat Kramer. He lived on my street and we used to fight every day. For fun. Monday he'd win, and Tuesday, I'd beat him silly, my knees on his shoulders, blam, blam, blam. Later on, he grew up, became a merchant marine, sailed all over the world, and then he used to race sailboats up and down both coasts—he had one he lived on—anything that floated, he wanted to sail. And he wasn't fat either. We just called him that . . . and boy, oh boy, if he was around now—ohhhh, would we go get those punks threw that egg at me. We'd run 'em into the ground. We'd kill 'em like dogs . . . poor little stupid ugly dogs, we'd cut out their hearts.

Rick. (*Suddenly coughing and coughing, having gulped down beer, and getting to his feet.*) Excuse me, Dad; excuse me. Listen, I've got to get going. You don't mind, do you. Got places to go; you're just talking nonsense anyway. (*He moves for the door.*)

Harriet. Have a good time, Rick.

Rick. I'm too pretty not to, Mom! (*And he is gone.*)

Ozzie. Where is he going? Where does he always go? Why does he always go and have some place to go? Always . . . !

Harriet. Just no never mind Ozzie. He's young and you're not. I'm going to do the dishes, but you just go right ahead with your little story and I'll listen from the kitchen. (*Gathering the beer and glasses she goes.*)

Ozzie. (*Following a little after her, not knowing quite what to do.*) I . . . outran a bowling ball. They bet I couldn't. (*And he starts as if at a sound. He turns toward*

DAVID.) What are you . . . looking . . . at? What do you think you're seeing?

DAVID. I'm not looking.

OZZIE. I feel watched; looked at.

DAVID. No.

OZZIE. Observed.

DAVID. I'm blind.

OZZIE. Did you do it? Had you anything to do with it?

DAVID. What?

OZZIE. That egg.

DAVID. I can't see.

OZZIE. I think you did. I feel like you did it.

DAVID. I don't have a car. I can't drive. How could I?

HARRIET. (*Hurrying in to clean up more of the party left-overs.*) Ohh, it's so good to hear men's voices in the house again, my two favorite men in all the world, it's what I live for really. Would you like some coffee? Oh, of course you would. Let me put some on. Your humble servant at your command, I do your bidding, bid me be gone. (*And she is gone without a pause, leaving* OZZIE *staring after her.*)

OZZIE. I could run again if I wanted. I'd . . . like . . . to want to. Christ, Fat Kramer is probably dead . . . now . . . not bouncing about in the ocean in some rattle-trap, tin-can joke of a ship . . . but dust . . . locked in a box . . . held in old . . . cold hands . . . And I just stand here, don't I? and let you talk any way you want. And Ricky gets up in the middle of some sentence I'm saying and walks right out and I let him. Because I fear him as I fear her . . . and you. Because I know the time is close when I will be of no use to any of you any longer. . . . and I am so frightened that if I do not seem inoffensive . . . and pleasant . . . if I am not careful to never disturb any of you unnecessarily, you will all abandon me. I can no longer compel recognition. I can no longer impose myself; make myself seen.

HARRIET. (*Entering now happily with a tray of coffee.*) Here you go. One for each and tea for me. Cream for

David . . . (*Setting a cup for* DAVID, *moving toward* OZZIE.) and cream and sugar for—

OZZIE. Christ how you must have beguiled me!

HARRIET. Pardon?

OZZIE. Beguiled and deceived!

HARRIET. Pardon . . . Ozzie . . . ?

OZZIE. And I don't even remember. I say "must" because I don't remember, I was so innocent, so childish in my strength, never seeing that it was surrendering I was doing, innocently and easily giving to you the love that was to return in time as flesh to imprison, detain, disarm and begin . . . to kill.

HARRIET. (*Examining him; scolding him.*) Ozzie, how many beers have you had? You've had too many beers!

OZZIE. Get away! (*He whirls to point at* DAVID *who sits on the floor facing upstage.*) Shut up! You've said enough! Detain and kill! Take and give nothing. It's what you meant, isn't it. You said it, a warning, nearly exactly this. This is your meaning!

DAVID. You're doing so well, Dad.

OZZIE. What? (*He doesn't understand.*)

DAVID. You're doing so well.

OZZIE. No.

DAVID. You are.

OZZIE. I'm doing awful. I'm doing terrible.

DAVID. This is the way you start, Dad. We'll be runners. Dad and Dave!

OZZIE. What's he saying?

HARRIET. My God, you're shaking; you're shaking.

OZZIE. I don't know what he's talking about. What's he talking about? (*To* HARRIET.) Just let me alone. Just please let me be. I don't really mean these things I'm saying. They're not really important. They'll go away and I don't mean them; they're just coming out of me; I'm just saying them, but I don't mean them. Oh, please, please, go away. (*And* DAVID, *behind them pivots to go up the stairs. She whirls, drawn by his sudden movement.*)

HARRIET. (*Dismayed.*) David . . . ?

DAVID. I'm going upstairs.

HARRIET. Oh, yes. Of course, of course.

DAVID. Just for a while.

HARRIET. Fine. Good. Of course.

DAVID. I'll see you all later. (*And he quietly enters his room, lies down.*)

OZZIE. (*Coiled on the couch, constricted with pain.*) I remember . . . there was a day . . . when I wanted to leave you, all of you, and I wanted desperately to leave, and I thought. "No. No," I couldn't. "Think of the children," I said. I meant something by that. I meant something and I understood it. But now . . . I don't. I no longer have it—that understanding. It's left me. What did I mean?

HARRIET. (*Approaching, a little fearful.*) You're trembling again. Look at you.

OZZIE. For a while . . . just a while, stay away. That's all I ask.

HARRIET. What? (*Reaching to touch him.*)

OZZIE. Stay the hell away from me!

HARRIET. Stay away? How far away? Ozzie, I'll move over . . . (*And she scurries, frightened.*) . . . here. Is this far enough away? Ozzie . . . ?

OZZIE. It's my hands; my feet. There's tiredness in me. I wake up each morning, it's in my fingers . . . sleep . . .

HARRIET. Ohhh, it's such a hateful thing in you the way you have no love for people different than yourself even when your son has come home to tell you of them; you have no right to carry on this way. He didn't bring her back—didn't marry her—we have those two things to thank God for. You've got to stop thinking only of yourself. We don't matter, only the children. When are you going to straighten out your thinking? You've got to straighten out your thinking.

OZZIE. I do. I know.

HARRIET. We don't matter; we're nothing. You're nothing, Ozzie. Only the children.

Ozzie. I know. I promise.

Harriet. All right . . . just . . . rest . . . for a little; I'll be back . . . (*As she is moving for the stairs.*)

Ozzie. I promise, Harriet.

Harriet. (*More to herself than to him.*) I'll go see how he is.

Ozzie. (*Coiled on the couch.*) It's my hands; they hurt . . . I want to wrap them; my feet . . .

Harriet. I'll tell him for you. I'll explain—how you didn't mean those terrible things you said. I'll explain.

Ozzie. It's going to be so cold; and I hurt . . . already . . . ; so cold; my ankles . . . !

Harriet. (*Hesitating on the stairway.*) Oh, Ozzie, Ozzie, we're all so worried, but I just think we must hope for the fine bright day coming when we'll be a family again as long as we try for what is good, truly for one another. Please. (*And as she is gone upstairs, the front door pops open and* Rick *comes bounding in.*)

Rick. Hi Mom, Hi, Dad.

Ozzie. Hi, Rick. Your Mom's upstairs. You have a nice time? I bet you did.

Rick. Fine; sure. How about you?

Ozzie. Fine; sure.

Rick. Whata you doin', restin'?

Ozzie. Workin'. Measurin'. Not everybody can play the guitar, you know. I'm going to build a wall . . . , I think; a wall. Pretty soon . . . Or . . . six walls. Thinkin' through the blue prints; lookin' over the plans.

Rick. (*Moving for the kitchen.*) I'm gonna get some fudge, you want some?

Ozzie. No. Too busy.

Rick. I had the greatest piece a tail tonight, Dad; I really did. What a beautiful piece a ass.

Ozzie. Did you, Rick?

Rick. She was bee-uuuuu-ti-ful.

Ozzie. Who was it?

Rick. Nobody you'd know, Dad.

Ozzie. Oh. Where'd you do it—I mean, get it.

RICK. In her car.

OZZIE. You were careful, I hope.

RICK. (*Laughing a little.*) C'mon, Dad.

OZZIE. I mean, it wasn't any decent girl.

RICK. Hell, no . . . , (*Still laughing, as* OZZIE *is getting to his feet.*)

OZZIE. (*Starting for the door.*) Had a dream of the guitar last night. It was huge as a building—all flecked with ice. You swung it in the air and I exploded.

RICK. I did?

OZZIE. Yes. I was gone.

RICK. Fantastic.

OZZIE. (*Exaggeratedly happy, almost singing.*) Goodnight.

(OZZIE *is gone out the door. BLACKOUT. MUSIC. Late night.* HARRIET *comes down the hall toward* DAVID's *room. She carries a towel, soap, a basin of water. Giving just the lightest tap on the door, she enters, smiling.*)

HARRIET. A little bath . . . David? A little sponge bath, all right? You must be all hot and sticky always in that bed. And we can talk. Why don't you take your shirt off? We've an awful lot to talk about. Take your shirt off, David. Your poor father . . . he has no patience; no strength. Something has to be done . . . A little sponge bath would be so nice. Have you talked to him lately? I think he thinks you're angry, for instance, with . . . us . . . for some reason . . . I don't know. (*Tugging at his shirt a little.*) Take your shirt off, David. You'll feel cool. That's all we've ever wanted, your father and me—good sweet things for you and Rick— ease and lovely child, a car, a wife, a good job. Time to relax and go to church on Sundays . . . and on holidays all the children and grand children come together, mingling—it would be so wonderful—everyone so happy— turkey. Twinkling lights. (*She is puzzled, a little wor-*

ried.) David, are you going to take your shirt off for me?

DAVID. They hit their children, did you know that? They hit them with sticks.

HARRIET. What?

DAVID. The yellow people. They punish the disobedience of their children with sticks. And then they sleep together one family in a bed, limbs all entwined like puppies. They work. I've seen them . . . laugh. They go on picnics. They murder—out of petty jealously. Young girls wet their cunts with spit when they are dry from wear and yet another G.I. stands in line. They spit on their hands and rub themselves, smiling, opening their arms.

HARRIET. That's not true.

DAVID. I saw—

HARRIET. (*Smilingly scolding him.*) None of what you say. No. No. All you did was something normal and regular, can't you see? And hundred of boys have done it before you. Thousands and thousands. Even now. Now. Now. Why do you have to be so sick and morbid about something so ordinary?

DAVID. She wasn't always a whore. Not always. Not—

HARRIET. If she is now, she was then only you didn't know. You didn't know. (*She is reaching for him, he eludes her, stands above her, as she is left sitting on the bed, looking up.*) Oh, David, David, I'm sure she was a lovely little girl but I would be insane if I didn't want you to marry someone of your own with whom you could be happy, if I didn't want grandchildren who could be free and welcome in their world. I couldn't want anything else, and still think I loved you. David, think of their faces, their poor funny little faces . . . (*And the cane is moving, slowly moving along the floor; it grazes her ankle.*)

DAVID. I know . . . I know . . . (*The cane moves now along her inner calf, rising under the hem of her robe, lifting. She tries to ignore it.*)

HARRIET. The human face was not meant to be that way. A nose is a thinness—you know that and the lips that are not thin are ugly, and it is we who disappear, David. They don't change and we are gone. It is our triumph, our whiteness. We disappear. What are you doing?— (*The cane has driven her back along the bed; no longer can it be ignored. It has pressed against her.*) They take us back and down if our children are theirs—it is not a mingling of blood, it is theft. (*And she hits the cane away. In revulsion she stands, wanting only to flee.*) Oh, you don't mean these awful things you do—your room stinks—odors come from under the door. You don't clean yourself. David, David, you've lost someone you love and it's pain for you, don't you see? I know, I know. But we will be the same, lost from you—you from us—and what will that gain for anyone? What?

(*Now the cane begins to scrape along the floor. It begins to lift and, shuddering, she flees down the hall. DAVID opens the door, listens. Stepping into the hall he quickly, carefully shuts the door, before moving down the stairs. In the living room, he moves in the dimness to plant himself before the front door where HARRIET will come, dressed in her robe and a raincoat and scarf, and when she sees him, she stops and nods, "Hello," and stands as he begins to advance upon her.*)

DAVID. Do you remember—? It was a Sunday when we had all gone to church and there was a young man there with his yellow wife and child. You spoke to us . . . , Dad and Rick and me as if we were conspirators. "I feel so sorry for that poor man—the baby looks like *her*," you said and your mouth twisted as if you had been forced to swallow someone else's spit.

HARRIET. No, no. You want only to hurt us, don't you. Isn't that right? That's all you want. Only to give us unhappiness. You cheat her, David. That lovely lovely

little girl you spoke of. She merits more to be done in
her memory than cruelty. (*She has seated herself on the
couch, clinging to some kind of normalcy, an odd and
eerie calmness upon both of them now.*)

DAVID. And I felt that I must go to her if I was to ever
live, and I felt that to touch truly her secret stranger's
tongue and mind would kill me. Now she will not forgive—the way I was.

HARRIET. (*Standing up.*) No. No, no. No, you don't
know how badly I feel. I've got a fever, the start of a cold
or flu. Let me be. I can't hardly . . . (*And she is moving away from him, back toward the stairs.*) move . . .
or stand up. I just want to flop somewhere and not have
to move. I'm so weak . . . don't hurt me anymore. Don't
hurt me—no more—I've got fever; please, fever; don't
hurt me. (*She is on the stairs.*)

DAVID. But I have so much to show you.

HARRIET. Who are you? I don't know who you are.
(*Stopped to stare helplessly down at him.*)

DAVID. David.

HARRIET. Noooooo.

DAVID. But I am.

HARRIET. No, no. Oh, no.

(*Moving now as in a trance,* HARRIET *walks up the stairs,
and into the hallway and down the hallway, all
slowly, while* ZUNG *comes forward in* DAVID'S *room
and* DAVID, *in the living room, calls after his mother.*)

DAVID. But it's what you want, don't you see? You can
see it. Her wrists are bound in coils of flowers. Flowers
strung in her hair, she hangs from the wind and men
strike and kick her. They are blind so that they may not
see her, yet they howl, wanting not to hurt her but only
as I do, to touch and hold her . . . and they howl . . . :
I'm home, Little David. . . . Home. (*And he is turning
now to take possession of the house. He will move to take
the space. A conquerer, he parades in the streets he has
taken: among the chairs, around the lamp.*) Little Davey

. . . of all the toys and tops and sailor suits, the plastic cards and tinker toys. Drum-player, bed-wetter, home-run-hitter, I'm home . . . now . . . and I want to drink from the toilet, wash there. (*On the stairs, he passes by the* GIRL *in his room, looking out. He follows in the way* HARRIET *has fled.*) And you will join me. You . . . will . . . join me!

(*As he goes the* GIRL *sits to gaze down upon the living room as the door opens.* OZZIE, *dressed in a suit or perhaps even a tuxedo, enters from the outside. Under his arm, he carries a packet of several hundred sheets of paper. He moves now with an absolute kind of confidence, almost smugness, as he carefully sets down the papers and proceeds to arrange three items of furniture—perhaps two chairs and a footstool—in such a way that they face him. Now he addresses them. He is cocky. "Harriet," he will say to the large chair. "David," he nods to the second chair. "Ricky," he will say, patting the footstool. And then, in the manner of the chairman of the board addressing the members of his board, he explains his position and plan of action for total solution. This is a kind of a commercial on the value of Ozzie.*)

OZZIE. Harriet. . . , David. . . , Ricky. (*He looks them over, the three empty chairs.*) I'm glad we've gotten finally together here, because the thing I've decided to do—and you all, hopefully, will understand my reasoning —is to *combat* the weariness beginning in me. It's like stepping into a hole, the way I feel each morning when I awaken, I see the day and the sun and I'm looking upward into the sky with a sense of looking down. A sense of hovering over a great pit into which I am about to fall. The sky. Foolishness and deceit, you say, and I know you're right; a trick of feeling inside me being played against me, seeking to diminish me and increase itself until it is larger than me filling me and who will I be then? It. That feeling of being nothing. At first . . . at first . . . I thought the thing to do would be to learn the guitar . . . But *that* I realized in just the nick of time was a folly that would have taken me into the very agony of frustration I was seeking to avoid. The skill to play like Ricky does is a great gift and only Ricky has it. He has no acids rotting his heart. He is all lies and music, his brain small and scaly, the brain of a snake forever innocent of the fact that it crawls. Lucky Ricky. But there are other things that people can do. And I've come at last to see the one that I must try if I am to become strong again in my opinion of myself. (*Holding up, with great oozing confidence, one of the many packets of paper.*) What I have here is an inventory of everything I own. Everything. Every stick of furniture, pot and pan, every sock, T. shirt, pen or pencil. And opposite is its price. For instance—here—that davenport—$512.98. That chair—$120.99. That table— (*He hurries to the table.*) —this table—$32.29. Etc. Etc. Now the idea is that you each carry a number of these at all times. (*He is now distributing more papers to the chairs, his control however, diminishing so that the papers are thrown about.*) Two or three copies, at all times and you are to pass them out at the slightest provocation. Let people know who I am, what I've done. Someone says to you, "Who are you?" You say, "I'm Ozzie's son." "I'm Ozzie's wife." "Who?" they'll say. "Take a look at that!" you tell 'em. Spit it out, give 'em a copy, turn on your heel and walk right out. That's the way I want it; from all of you from here on out, that's the WAY I WANT IT! (*And the room goes suddenly into eerie light. And the* GIRL *is high behind him in* DAVID'S *room, hit with a sudden light that makes* OZZIE *go rigid as if some current from her has entered into him and he is turning slowly to look up at her.*) Let him alone. Let David alone.

(HARRIET *is in the hallway.*)

HARRIET. Is there any aspirin down there? I don't feel

well . . . Ozzie. I don't feel well at all. David poked me with his cane and I don't like . . . what's . . . going on. (OZZIE *is only staring at the* GIRL.) I don't want what's happening to happen. (*She has halted on the stairway.*) It must be some awful flu. I'm so weak, or some awful cold. There's an odor . . .

OZZIE. I'll go to the drugstore. My eyes hurt, funny . . .

HARRIET. Oh, Ozzie . . . oh my God. It was awful. I can't help it. He's crazy—he—

OZZIE. I don't want to hear about him. I don't want to hear. Oh, no, oh, no. I can't. No more, no more. Let him do what he wants. No more of him; no more. Just you —you're all that I can see. All that I care for or want. (*He has moved to her as she moves down and they embrace.*)

HARRIET. David's crazy . . . !

OZZIE. You're everything.

HARRIET. Please . . .

OZZIE. Listen; we must hide; please.

HARRIET. (*As she is moving to kneel, and he, while helping her, kneels also.*) Pray with me.

OZZIE. We won't move. We'll hide by not moving.

HARRIET. We must beg God to not turn against him; convince him. Ozzie, pray . . . !

OZZIE. Yes . . . !

HARRIET. Now . . . !

(*They pray: kneeling, murmuring, and it goes on and on. The door opens.*)

RICK. Hi, Mom; hi, Dad. (*They continue. He stops, stares.*) Hi . . . Mom; hi, Dad . . . (*He is very puzzled.*) Hi . . . Mom . . . hi . . . Dad . . . (*He thinks and thinks.*) David. (*He screams at* DAVID, *he goes running up to look in* DAVID'S *room, but the room is empty,* DAVID, *in ragged combat fatigues, appears on the top of the stairs.* RICK *frightened, backs away.*) Dave . . . what have you got to say for yourself? What can you?

Honest ta God, I've had it. I really have. I can't help it,
even if you are sick, and I hate to complain, but you're
getting them so mixed up they're not themselves anymore. Just a minute ago—one minute—they were on their
knees, do you know that? Just a minute ago—right here
on the living room floor, now what's the point of that?
They're my mom and dad, too.

DAVID. He doesn't know, does he, Dad? Did you hear
him?

RICK. Let Dad alone.

DAVID. He doesn't know how when you finally see
yourself, there's nothing really there to see . . . isn't
that right? Mom? (*He stands on the landing, looking
down upon them.*)

RICK. Dave, honest to God, I'm warning you, let them
alone.

DAVID. (DAVID *is decending now, the* GIRL *behind him.
Calmly he speaks, growing slowly happy.*) Do you know
how north of here on farms gentle loving dogs are raised,
while in the forests, other dogs run wild. And upon oc-
casion, one of those that's wild is captured and put in
among the others that are tame, bringing with it the
memory of when they had all been wild—the dark and
terror—that had made them wolves. Don't you hear
them? (*And there is a rumbling.*)

RICK. What? Hear what?

(*It is wind-like, the rumbling of many trucks.*)

DAVID. Don't you hear the trucks? They're all over
town, lined up from the center of town into the country.
Don't you hear? They've stopped bringing back the
blind. They're bringing back the dead now. The convoy's
broken up. There's no control . . . they're walking from
house to house, through the shrubbery, under the trees,
carrying one of the dead in a bright blue rubber bag for
which they have no papers, no name or number. No one
knows whose it is. They're at the Jensen's now. Now Al
Jensen's at the door, all his kids behind him trying to

peek. Al looks for a long long time into the open bag before he shakes his head. They zipper shut the bag and turn away. They've been to the Mayer's the Kelly's, the Irwin's and Kresses. They'll be here soon.

OZZIE. Nooo.

DAVID. And Dad's going to let them in. We're going to let them in.

HARRIET. What's he saying?

DAVID. He's going to knock.

OZZIE. I DON'T KNOW.

DAVID. Yes. Yes. (*A knocking sound. Is it* DAVID *knocking with his fist against the door or table?*)

OZZIE. Nooooo.

RICK. Mom, he's driving Dad crazy. (*Knocking loud: it seems the front door.*)

OZZIE. David, will I die? (*Moving toward the door.*)

HARRIET. Who do you suppose it could be so late?

RICK. I don't think you should just go opening the door to anybody this time of the night, there's no telling who it might be. (*Intercepting his* DAD, *blocking the way to the door.*)

DAVID. We know who it is.

OZZIE. Oh, David, why can't you wait? Why can't you rest?

DAVID. (*But* DAVID *is the father now, and he will explain, he loves them all.*) Look at her. See her, Dad. Tell her to go to the door. Tell her yes, it's your house, you want her to open the door and let them in. Tell her yes, the one with no name is ours. We'll put it in that chair. We can bring them all here. I want them all here, all the trucks and bodies. There's room. Ricky can sing. (*Handing* RICK *the guitar.*) We'll stack them along the walls . . .

OZZIE. Nooo . . .

DAVID. Pile them over the floor . . .

OZZIE. . . . no, no . . .

DAVID. They will become the floor and they will become the walls, the chairs. We'll sit in them, sleep. We

will call them "home." We will give them as gifts—call
them "ring" and "pot" and "cup." No, no; it's not a
thing to fear . . . we will notice them no more than all
the others. (*He is gentle, happy, consoling to them.*)

OZZIE. What others? There are no others. (*And* OZZIE
scurries to the T.V. where it sits beneath the stairs.) . . . I'll
get it fixed. I'll fix it. Who needs to hear it? We'll watch it.
(*Wildly turning T.V. channels.*) I flick my rotten life. Oh,
there's a good one. Look at that one. Ohhh, isn't that a good
one? That's the best one. That's the best one.

DAVID. They will call it madness. We will call it seeing.
(*Calmly* DAVID *lifts* OZZIE.)

OZZIE. I don't want to disappear.

DAVID. Let her take you to the door. We will be
runners. You will have eyes.

OZZIE. I will be blind. I will disappear.

(*KNOCKING again. Again.*)

DAVID. You stand and she stands. "Let her go," you
say; "she is garbage and filth and you must get her back
if you wish to live. She is sickness. You must cherish
her." Old voices you have trusted all your life as if they
were your own, speaking always friendly. "She's all of
everything impossible made possible!"

OZZIE. Ricky . . . . nooo . . . !

DAVID. Don't call to Ricky. You love her. You will
embrace her, see her and—

OZZIE. He has no right to do this to me.

DAVID. Don't call to Ricky!

OZZIE. (*Suddenly raging, rushing at* DAVID, *pushing
him.*) You have no right to do this.

RICK. Noooooo! (*Savagely smashing his guitar down
upon* DAVID *who crumples.*) Let Dad alone. Let him
alone. He's sick of you. What the hell's a matter with
you? He doesn't wanna talk anymore about all the
stupid stuff you talk. He wants to talk about cake and
cookies and cars and coffee. He's sick a you and he wants

you to shut up. We hate you, goddamn you. (*Silence: DAVID lies still.*)

ZUNG. Chào ông! (OZZIE *pivots, looks at her.*) Chào ông! Hôm nay ông manh không?

OZZIE. Oh, what is it that you want? I'm tired, I mean it. Forgive me. I'm sick of the sight of you, squatting all the time. In filth like animals, talking gibberish, your breath sick with rot . . . And yet you look at me with those sad appealing eyes as if there is some real thing that can come between us when you're not even here. You are deceit. (*His hands, rising, have driven to her throat. The fingers close.*) I'm not David. I'm not silly and soft . . . little David. The sight of you sickens me. YOU HEAR ME, DAVID? Believe me. I am speaking my honest true feelings. I spit on you, the both of you, I piss on your eyes and pain. Flesh is lies. You are garbage and filth. You are darkness. I cast you down. Deceit. Animal. Dirty animal. (*And he is over her. They are sprawled on the ground. Silence as no one moves. The girl lies like a rag beneath him.*)

RICK. I saw this really funny movie last night . . . This really . . . funny, funny movie about this young couple and they were going to get a divorce but they didn't. It was really funny.

(OZZIE *is hiding the girl: either dragging her behind the couch, or putting her in a green garbage bag brought to him by HARRIET.*

HARRIET. What's that? What's that?

RICK. This movie I saw.

HARRIET. Anybody want to go for groceries? We need Kleenex, sugar, milk.

RICK. What a really funny movie.

OZZIE. I'll go; I'll go.

HARRIET. Good. Good.

OZZIE. I think I saw it on T.V.

(*They are cleaning up their house now, putting the chairs back in order, dumping all of* OZZIE's *leaflets in the waste can.*)

HARRIET. Did you enjoy it, Rick?

RICK. Oh, yeah. I loved it.

OZZIE. I laughed so much I almost got sick. It was really good. I laughed.

RICK. I bet it was; I bet you did.

OZZIE. Oh, I did. (*Even* DAVID *helps: getting himself off the floor and seated in a chair.*)

HARRIET. How are you feeling, Ricky?

RICK. Fine.

HARRIET. Good.

RICK. How do you feel?

HARRIET. Oh, I'm all right. I feel fine.

OZZIE. Me, too. I feel fine, too. What day is it, anyway? Monday?

HARRIET. Wednesday.

RICK. Tuesday, Mom. (*Now all three are seated on the couch.*)

OZZIE. I thought it was Monday.

RICK. Oh, no.

HARRIET. No, no. You're home now, David . . .

RICK. (*Moving to* DAVID *who sits alone in a chair.*) Hey, Dave, listen, will you, I mean I know it's not my place to speak out and give advice and everything because I'm the youngest, but I just gotta say my honest true feelings and I'd kill myself if I were you, Dave. You're in too much misery. I'd cut my wrists. Honestly speaking, brother to brother, you should have done it long ago. (*As* DAVID *is looking about.*) You looking for her? She's not here.

DAVID. What?

RICK. Nooo. She's never been here. You just thought so. You decided not to bring her, Dave, remember? You decided, all things considered that you preferred to come back without her. Too much risk and inconvenience . . . you decided. Isn't that right. Sure. You know it is. You've always known. (*Silence:* HARRIET *moves to look out the front door.*) Do you want to use my razor, Dave? I have one right here and you can use it if you want. (DAVID *seems to be looking at the razor.*) Just take it if you want it, Dave.

HARRIET. Go ahead, David. The front yard's empty. You don't have to be afraid. The streets, too . . . still and empty.

RICK. It doesn't hurt like you think it will. Go ahead; just take it, Dave.

OZZIE. You might as well.

RICK. That's right.

OZZIE. You'll feel better.

RICK. I'll help you now, Dave, ok.

HARRIET. I'll go get some pans and towels.

RICK. (*Moving about* DAVID, *patting him, buddying him.*) Oh, you're so confused, you don't know what to do. It's just a good thing I got this razor, boy, that's all I gotta say. You're so confused. You see, Dave, where you're wrong is your point of view, it's silly. It's just really comical because you think people are valuable or something and given a chance like you were to mess with 'em, to take a young girl like that and turn her into a whore, you shouldn't when of course you should or at least might . . . on whim . . . you see? I mean, you're all backwards, Dave—you're upside down. You don't know how to go easy and play—I bet you didn't have any fun the whole time you were over there—no fun at all—and it was there. I got this buddy Gerry, he was there, and he used to throw bags of cement at 'em from off the back a his truck. They'd go whizzin' through those villages, throwin' off these bags a cement. You could kill people, he says, you hit 'em right. Especially the kids. There was this once they knocked this ole man off his bicycle—fifty pounds a dry cement—and then the back a the truck got his legs. It was hysterical—can't you just see that, Dave? Him layin' there howlin', all the guys in the truck bowin' and wavin' and tippin' their hats. What a goddamn funny story, huh?

(HARRIET *has brought silver pans and towels with roosters on them. The towels cover the arms of the chair and* DAVID'S *lap. The pans will catch the blood. All has been neatly placed.* DAVID, *with* RICKY'S *help, will cut one wrist, then the other.*)

DAVID. I wanted . . . to kill you . . . all of you.

RICK. I know, I know; but you're hurt; too weak.

DAVID. I wanted for you to need what I had and I wouldn't give it.

HARRIET. That's not possible.

OZZIE. Nooooo.

DAVID. I wanted to get you. Like poor bug eyed fish flung up from the brief water to the lasting dirt, I would gut you.

HARRIET. David, no, no, you didn't want that.

OZZIE. No, no.

RICK. I don't even know why you'd think you did.

OZZIE. We kill you is what happens.

RICK. That's right.

OZZIE. And then, of course, we die, too. . . . Later on, I mean. And nothing stops it. Not words . . . or walls . . . or even guitars.

RICK. Sure.

OZZIE. That's what happens.

HARRIET. It isn't too bad, is it?

RICK. How bad is it?

OZZIE. He's getting weaker.

HARRIET. And in a little, it'll all be over. You'll feel so grand. No more funny talk.

RICK. You can shower; put on clean clothes. I've got deodorant you can borrow. "After Roses," Dave. The scent of a thousand roses. (*Preparing to take a picture: crouching, aiming.*)

HARRIET. Take off your glasses, David.

OZZIE. Do as you're told.

RICK. (*As* DAVID'S *hands are rising toward the glasses to remove them.*) I bet when you were away there was only plain water to wash in, huh? You probably hadda wash in the rain. (*Taking the picture. Flash, slide: close-up of* DAVID'S *face, nothing visible but the face. It is the slide of* DAVID *that, appearing at the very start of the play, was referred to as "somebody sick." Now it hovers, stricken, sightless, revealed.*) Mom, I like David like this.

HARRIET. He's happier.

OZZIE. We're all happier.

RICK. Too bad he's gonna die.

OZZIE. No, no; he's not gonna die, Rick. He's only gonna nearly die. Only nearly.

RICK. Ohhhhhhhhhhh.

HARRIET. Mmmmmmmmmmmmm.

(*And* RICK, *sitting, begins to play his guitar for* DAVID, *and the music is alive and fast. It has a rhythm, a drive of happiness that is contagious. The LIGHTS SLOWLY FADE.*)

PROP LIST

Sofa
Coffee table
T.V.
2 arm chairs
footstool
side table
bar/desk unit
small stool
coat rack
lamp
bed
bedroom chair
table
lamp

ACT ONE

Oɴsᴛᴀɢᴇ Pʀᴇ-Sᴇᴛ:
  Sofa:
    3 pillows
  Coffee table:
    Sewing bag and sewing
    Ashtray with matches
    Newspaper
  Side table:
    Ashtray
    Comic books
    "Popular Mechanics" magazine
    Cigarettes and matches
    Screwdriver
  Bar unit (desk):
    Telephone
    Telephone book
    Camera and flashcube
    Pushbutton phone directory
    Ashtray
    Pencil cup with pens

In drawer:
Bottle of aspirin
"Meyers" spot remover
Dust cloth
Bedroom chair:
Necktie

ACT TWO

ONSTAGE PRE-SET:
  Coffee table:
    Same as ACT ONE
    Add: "Popular Mechanics"
    Pack of Cigarettes
  Side table:
    Camera and flashcube
    Black lettercase with "Psychology Today" magazine

S. L. PROPTABLE (below):
  Clipboard
  Pen
  Manila envelope
  Shipping receipt
  Flashcube
  3 packages of printed lists of Ozzie's possessions

S. L. PROPTABLE (above):
  Razor cap
  Arm pad
  Basin of water
  Towel
  Sponge
  Box of film
  Box of flashcubes
  1 movie projector
  Crossword puzzle book
  Pencil

S. R. PROPTABLE:
  Basketball
  Bowl of pretzels
  Bowl of potato chips
  Half grapefruit in bowl
  3 small plates of fudge

Small tray with glass of juice, bowl of soup, spoon and napkin
Mug of coffee
Candle in holder
Matches
Half glass of soda
Half bottle of soda
Small tray with 2 glasses of milk, 2 plates of fudge
Tray with 2 cups of regular coffee, 1 cup of tea
1 cup of coffee with saucer
Tray with party items:
   Cake, 4 slices cut
   Cake cutter
   4 plates
   4 forks
   Napkins
   3 glasses of soda
Razor
Break away guitar
Rosary
3 school books
2 cookies
1 saucer with 2 pieces of fudge
Large basin of water
3 small hand towels
Tray with 2 glasses of beer
Bowl of peanuts

PERSONAL PROPS:
   Ricky—guitar and car keys
   David—cane and dark glasses
   Ozzie—handkerchief

COSTUME LIST

ACT ONE

OZZIE:
  Slacks, shirt, cardigan sweater, shoes

HARRIET:
  Skirt, blouse, cardigan sweater, shoes, apron, house robe, slippers, nightgown robe, raincoat

RICKY:
  Slacks, turtleneck shirt, leather vest, low boots, velvet slacks, flowered shirt, leather jacket

DAVID:
  Regulation army uniform, pajamas, bathrobe, necktie, slippers/shoes

SGT. MAJOR:
  Regulation army uniform

FATHER D.:
  Sweatshirt, jacket, tennis shoes

ZUNG:
Samuel French—Sticks and Bones—gef

ACT TWO

OZZIE:
  Dress suit, white shirt, cardigan sweater, windbreaker jacket, raincoat, bow tie

HARRIET:
  3 piece knit suit
  Nightgown and robe—Act I
  Skirt and blouse, sweater—Act I

DAVID:
  Slacks, T-shirt, pullover sweater, loafers, army jungle fatigue uniform with boots

FATHER D.:
  Black cassock, white collar, black shoes, jacket

LYRICS BY
DAVID RABE

"BABY WHEN I FIND YOU"

MUSIC BY
GALT MacDERMOT

BA-BY, WHEN I FIND YOU,— NEV-ER GON - NA STAND BE-HIND YOU,

GON-NA, GON-NA LEAD YOU, SOFT-LY AT THE START, GENT-LY BY THE HEART, SWEET

LOVE! SLIP-PING SOFT-LY TO THE SEA YOU AND ME BOTH MINE,

WON-DROUS AS A GREEN GROW-ING FOR-EST VINE. BA-BY, WHEN I FIND YOU,

NEV-ER GON - NA STAND BE-HIND YOU. GON-NA, GON-NA LEAD YOU.

SOFT-LY AT THE START, GENT-LY BY THE HEART, SWEET LOVE!

BA-BY, WHEN I FIND YOU.....

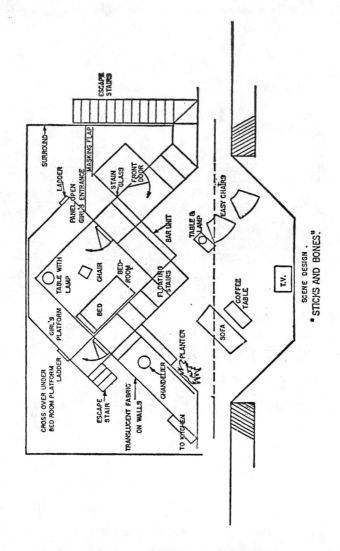

SCENE DESIGN.
"STICKS AND BONES."

96